Bellevue
Literary
Review

*A journal of humanity
and human experience*

Volume 5, Number 1, Spring 2005
Department of Medicine
New York University School of Medicine
www.BLReview.org

The *Bellevue Literary Review* is published twice a year by the Department of Medicine at New York University School of Medicine.

Subscriptions available at www.BLReview.org (1 year: $12 ♦ 3 years: $30)

The Editors invite submissions of previously unpublished works of fiction, nonfiction, and poetry that touch upon relationships to the human body, illness, health, and healing. We encourage creative interpretation of these themes. Manuscripts can be submitted at www.BLReview.org.

The Editorial Staff of the *Bellevue Literary Review* express its deep appreciation to the following people who have assisted with editorial review: Sonya Abrams, Sarah Bain, David Baldwin, Robin Black, Denitza Blagev, Toby Leah Bochan, Andrew Bomback, Carlos Caprioli, Ana Chavier, Marcia Day Childress, Rebecca Dillingham, Steven Field, Serena Fox, Heather Genovese, Madina Gerasimov, Harvey Greenberg, Heather Hewett, Meghan Hickey, Marie Holmes, David Hong, Jackie Keer, April Krassner, Florence Kugel, Katrina Lust, Suzanne McConnell, Elayne Mustalish, Ruth Oratz, Marco Rafala, Pamela Rosenthal, Benjamin Sadock, Peter Selgin, Shetal Shah, Jon Soverow, Jana Unkel, Benj Vardigan, Lisa Voltolina, Valerie Witte, and Carol Zoref.

The BLR gratefully acknowledges the Lucius N. Littauer Foundation and the Council for Literary Magazines and Presses (CLMP) for their generous support.

We also thank Dorothy Harris, Michael Becton, and the staff of Bellevue Hospital; Lorinda Klein, and the Ragdale Foundation.

Cover Note: Until the middle of the twentieth century, women with resources gave birth at home, with a personal physician or midwife on hand. It was only the indigents and immigrants who went to the hospital to have their babies. Bellevue's Emergency Pavilion was established in 1877 by the Nursing Schools Board of Managers for "women taken in labor on the streets." This pavilion was a small, two-story, converted firehouse at 223 East 26th Street (now a non-descript Department of Sanitation building). During their required six-week rotation there, physicians were permitted no contact with the main hospital several blocks away to prevent spread of puerperal fever to the new mothers.

The cover photo shows student nurses caring for babies in their bassinets (c. 1915). The students were advised by the Board of Managers to watch the babies carefully when they were distributed to their mothers at feeding time since there was a high incidence of infanticide. The Emergency Pavilion closed in 1935 and all cases were transferred to the newly built F&G pavilion at the main hospital campus. New licensing laws and the emerging field of obstetrics for doctors heated up the politics of childbirth, and Bellevue's School of Midwifery closed its doors that same year. (The F&G pavilion was replaced in 1973 with the "New Bellevue" building, where all in-patients are currently housed.)

Bellevue Literary Review

A journal of humanity and human experience

Danielle Ofri — *Editor-in-Chief*
Ronna Wineberg — *Fiction Editor*
Jerome Lowenstein — *Nonfiction Editor*
Roxanna Font — *Poetry Editor*
Donna Baier Stein — *Poetry Editor*
Stacy Bodziak — *Managing Editor*
Corie Feiner — *Assistant Editor*
Frances Richey — *Assistant Editor*

Martin J. Blaser — *Publisher*

Doris Milman — *Copy Editor*
Troi Santos — *Graphic Designer*
Lucy Cribben — *Department Administrator*
Melissa Flanagan — *Development Manager*
Elsa Nunez — *Office Associate*
Nisha Gupta, Danielle Newman, Claire Schwartz — *Interns*

Contents

Volume 5, Number 1, Spring 2005

Fiction

Nonfiction

Poetry

Foreword

One of the most pleasurable tasks of editing a literary journal is assigning the order of the writings in a particular issue. After months of hard work by all of the reviewers and editors—culling the selections, editing the pieces, working with the authors, copy editing, proofreading, formatting—there is the final step: deciding the order of placement. For this issue, I spread out the 36 poems, stories, and essays on the brown vinyl examination table in my clinic office at Bellevue, pulling out the footrest to accommodate extra pages. It is a heady experience to be surrounded by such richness of literature; as with the Viennese dessert tables at fancy weddings, it is hard to know where to begin.

I moved the pages around, trying to match themes and writing styles, wondering which order would best engage a reader. Despite my best efforts to remain focused on the task of layout, time and again I would find myself reading a now-familiar story or poem, recalling the joy of the editors in selecting that piece.

As I tried to match prose and poems, I realized that there were many more poems than prose pieces that dealt with death. A number of the stories and essays considered issues of mortality, but most were not about death, per se, certainly not as many as there were poems.

How did the balance come to be skewed toward poetry? The *Bellevue Literary Review* receives hundreds of stories and essays that concern death, and often it is difficult to reject these manuscripts, particularly the nonfiction. But it seems to be very hard to write well about death. Narrating the details of death runs a fine line: the concepts are profound, yet the actual process can be surprisingly ordinary, and if not illuminated in some unique or literary manner, runs the risk of being almost clichéd. Might poetry be more amenable than prose to writing (well) about death?

The poems in this issue that deal with death suggest that poetry, by its ability to tease out a single strand of emotion, is able to be removed from the "mere" recounting of death. By offering a simple, arresting image, a poem allows us to meditate on a specific aspect of death. With metaphor we can access a sliver of insight, which is easier to fathom than the frightening black hole that death can be.

Judy Katz's pair of poems, *Anniversary* and *The Weight of Absence*, offer images of loss that are, in some ways, more realistic than fact-based accounts of death. "When you died," she writes, "our house sank deeper into the earth…" In the poem *Medicine Chest*, Amanda Auchter contemplates the simple act of cleaning out the medicine chest after the death of a spouse, of wiping away fingerprints on the mirror, of erasing the last traces of presence. Rebecca McClanahan's poem *Gesture* looks toward the Pietà, the iconic image of a mother holding a son, and then wonders how a son should hold his mother when it is *she* who is dying.

While the spareness of poetry is often the key to concise imagery, good fiction—despite its "wordiness"—can often seize a potent image. *His Own Time*, by John Thompson, takes place in a prison in which one inmate has decided to end it all. How the other prisoners view this is anything but cliché. The main character in *The Committal*, by Alice Ayers, sits with her mother, for the umpteenth time, as her mother plans what should happen upon her death. "She loves to plan any trip: Paris, Madrid, Egypt, Antarctica, China. Why should her funeral be any different? Just another itinerary to draw up."

Most of the prose in this issue of the *Bellevue Literary Review*, however, does not deal with death. Two pieces look at birth. Angela Wheelock's essay *Nesting in a Season of Light* recounts the harrowing experience of trying to get pregnant, set against the lush, natural rhythms of the Yukon. *Baby*, by Lois Taylor, begins with the equally harrowing experience of miscarriage, this set against historical rigidities of class, race, and sex.

Beginnings, though, are not limited to birth. The poems by Floyd Skloot— *First Steps* and *Midnight in the Alzheimer's Suite*—hint that epiphanies can be found in the least likely of settings, as long as one's ear is appropriately attuned.

Several selections examine young people who are facing disease. Steven Schwartz's protagonist in *Opposite Ends of the World* is struggling to retain his self-definition in the face of multiple sclerosis. In *The Bald and the Beautiful*, William Bradley recounts how daytime soap operas were a critical component of his treatment for Hodgkin's disease. The narrator of Whitney Scharer's story *Erosion* decides to keep her ear tumor a secret so she can keep up with her friends on a desert hike. Seth Carey's essay, *The Absolute Worst Thing*, about life with ALS (amyotrophic lateral sclerosis), was written using the blinks of his eye to select letters on a special computer.

We hope you find the diverse writings in this issue of the *Bellevue Literary Review* both enjoyable and stimulating, and that the images will remain with you long after the cover is closed.

Danielle Ofri, MD, PhD
Editor-in-Chief

His Own Time

John Thompson

There's something about this waitress that keeps me coming back here. Part of the draw is obvious: it's her hair. I've never seen anything like it. It's braided into a ponytail that hangs like an auburn rope along her back. I'm hoping to get up the nerve to ask her out. She wipes a table, straightens up, and whips the braid of hair over her shoulder. From where I sit, it appears to come dangerously close to the blades of the ceiling fan. It's an illusion. I know that. Even so, an image ambushes me, her hair snarled in the blades and her body yanked off the floor, her pretty legs flopping as she hangs from the makeshift gallows. I turn back to the bar to try to clear my head.

I did a little time once. It wasn't a long bit, but that doesn't matter much. Time is time. One day a new guy on the block, Lenny, decides he can't take it anymore. Some men are playing cards, and some are walking in circles around the perimeter of the cellblock. You'd be surprised how much time you can kill walking in circles. Most guys walk with somebody. I think it's so they don't look crazy. You hear guys say how they walked with so and so for seven years at some joint or another. That's what "walking with" means. And there's a certain stride and pace. It's not for exercise; it's to kill time. I can spot a man on the street with the stride and know he's done time. It's a sort of shuffle that keeps you moving, but there's no hurry because there's no destination.

Me, on this day, I'm reading a book. I'm thinking it was *Zorba the Greek,* but I'm not so sure. Some guys walk away the months; I read away the minutes. I'd read anything I could get my hands on just to lose myself in something. Anyway, I'm reading and the last thing I have on my mind is Lenny and his problems. There's a saying, "Do your own time," and that's exactly what I intend to do.

Only this guy Lenny makes it hard to ignore what he's up to, which is to off himself. I don't know why he wants to exactly, there could be a hundred reasons, or no reason at all other than you're in a place like this, but it ought to be a private thing, at the very least done at nighttime. Lenny's got a sheet all twisted up into a rope and he's dragging his desk from his cell to the end of the block where there's a pipe. When he passes by my cell he's mumbling something to himself about how he'd be better off dead, or maybe I'd have never noticed. Then he gets in place and spends a minute or two checking the layout. He climbs on the desk and drapes the sheet over the pipe. It's funny what I remember next.

The normal roar of the cellblock starts to quiet a little at a time now. It was like a factory I worked in once. At break time you could hear the plant wind down incrementally as each machine shut off, only on the cellblock the roar winds down as each con notices Lenny and shuts up to watch the show.

Lenny is in place. He throws the sheet rope over the pipe, and then pulls a snug knot to the drainpipe. I'm thinking that if he does wrap the noose end around his neck and jumps off the desk, the sewer pipe will break and shit will pour onto the block and stink it up worse than normal, because I can't really believe that Lenny will succeed at this anymore than he's succeeded at anything else in his sorry life.

He isn't even a decent criminal. Lenny is in prison for stealing copper wire. He and a cousin would go into the woods and pull down the wire to hunting camps and cabins. They'd cut down hundreds of feet of wire at a time, roll the mess up through the woods, over rough mountainous terrain that was filled with poison ivy and other shit. Then they'd drag the coils of wire into a truck. They'd drive it home, burn the insulation off in their backyard, and then haul it another fifty miles to a scrap yard to sell it for 39 stinking cents a pound. A real fucking job would have been less work. Even so, they'd managed to get busted because they helped themselves to the liquor in the hunting camp and passed out on the front stoop of the lodge. To top it off, the hunting lodge belonged to a politician so Lenny got the maximum sentence. I can't think of Lenny without thinking of *Cool Hand Luke* and Paul Newman breaking into parking meters to get himself locked up. Only Lenny is no cool hand anything. Lenny is a fuck-up, pure and simple. A likeable fuck-up, sure, but a fuck-up nonetheless.

Lenny's got the noose around his neck and he's poised on the edge of the desk. I put my book down and sit up in my bunk. He hesitates and readjusts the noose so the knot is on the side of his head. I'm not sure what difference it makes, but it seems important to him. He reaches up and checks the knot at the pipe, which seems okay. Then he turns his head back and forth like he's getting comfortable in a dentist chair headrest. Finally, somebody from the other end of the block yells, "What the fuck do you think you're doing?"

Lenny ignores this and tugs on the sheet again, checking the strength of the pipe. He seems satisfied and moves back to the edge of the desk. He's in position and seems ready.

I wait. The whole cellblock waits. I'm getting angry, though I'm not exactly sure why. Lenny just pisses me off. He readjusts the sheet again at the pipe. I don't want this to happen; mostly I don't want to think about it. I get more pissed off the more he stalls, and apparently I'm not the only one. Morgan slams his cards down, "Jesus Christ."

Every cellblock in every prison has a con who runs the show. Morgan runs this one. It's not that he's the toughest dude on the block; I doubt that he is, but the toughest dudes look to him and do what he says. He's a career criminal and proud of it. Morgan's smart, too. He talks to me because I read more than comic books. Morgan has given himself quite an education here; during his times of incarceration he's read most of the classics. It's all part of the life in the can. Morgan claims he'd take a year on the inside if he had to, for every ten on the street living the way he wants. That is, by his own rules.

Morgan's also got a mean streak. He lists the aluminum baseball bat as one of the century's greatest inventions. A man can hear the whistle from the bat before it hits the kneecap, he told me. So even if the man he's punishing closes his eyes, he can still hear it coming, and Morgan likes that.

Morgan gets up from the card game. "Get the fuck down from there asshole. You're not going to do anything." I'm glad Morgan is going to put an end to this charade.

Lenny, his voice a little gargled from the constriction of the bed sheet around his throat, says, "I am, too."

"Well then what's the hold up?" says Morgan. "You're fucking up my game here."

Lenny doesn't seem to have a response, but his eyes grow more doe-like.

"Well?" Morgan starts to amble toward Lenny, reaching into his shirt pocket for his Marlboros.

"Leave me alone," says Lenny.

Morgan holds the cigarette pack out in a friendly gesture. "Relax," he says. "I'm not going to stop you. I'm just offering you a last smoke. That's all."

Lenny is shaking now. Facing Morgan is worse than facing death.

"Here." Morgan offers the pack with a cigarette tapped out and easy to grab.

Lenny takes the cigarette and Morgan lights his own and then holds the match up high enough so Lenny can get a light, which is pretty high, since Lenny's head is tethered to the pipe. Lenny inhales. I figured maybe everything is going to be okay and we can go back to doing our time in peace. That's when Morgan asks Lenny if he really wants to die and Lenny says, "Yeah."

Morgan steps back a little and as calmly as could be says, "Then die you pussy motherfucker," and kicks the desk out from under Lenny. Lenny's body drops the few inches of slack in his makeshift rope. Morgan turns away after the kick and starts back to the card game without looking at Lenny who, as it turns out, didn't really want to die and is flopping and kicking while grabbing onto the rope with both hands, fighting for life. The cellblock is as quiet as I'd ever heard it as Morgan gets to the table and says, "Deal."

Nobody looks at Lenny as he fights the fight of his life, trying not to choke. But we all hear him gurgle and kick, his feet banging at the wall trying to get a toehold. It's as if Lenny had never existed and isn't at the end of his rope in the back of the cellblock.

The next sound I hear is the cards shuffle then slap to the table for somebody to cut. Nobody even looks in Lenny's direction. Me, I'm no better than anybody else. I hate Lenny's guts. I go back to my book. I don't watch and I don't help. What does it matter really?

The waitress's hip brushes against my arm, and I pull away as if her touch had cut like a shiv. I shake it off and come back to the present. When she puts in her drink order, I lean back to look at that tantalizing rope of hair and I know I'm never going to ask her out as I had planned. I mean, who am I kidding? I couldn't look at her without thinking of that place and Lenny. Always pushing away that image. When she turns to take the drinks to a table, I throw a buck on the bar and walk beside her stride for stride. Then she stops to serve a drink, and I keep on walking. After all, a man has to do his own time. ଛ

The Committal

Alice Ayers

"Come here." It's the third week of my yearly trip back to South Carolina, and my mother is calling me to the living room. "Sit," she says, and pats the space next to her on the couch. *The Book of Common Prayer* is in her hands, open to the committal service. She loves to plan any trip: Paris, Madrid, Egypt, Antarctica, China. Why should her funeral be any different? Just another itinerary to draw up. "Gene, do take those children outside," she says. I unhook one daughter from my ankle, let the other slide from my hip. They are whiny today, demanding food different from what she keeps in her house, entertainment, a constant, shouting TV. They go pouting into the backyard with my father, under the same pines where I played as a child, the same pine needle duff poking at their bare feet. My father opens a lawn chair. Angie, the five-year-old, dumps herself on the ground, arms folded. Nell, younger, more willing to please, wiggles in the grass like a pup.

My mother pats the couch again. I sit, take the book from her hands. She's been annotating the committal service for years. The pages are dark with her crooked scrawl, pencil smears, scratch-outs, marginalia.

My mother and I may know each other more than we know any one else. Sometimes I think I know her more. The second of four children, hungry for her affection, I studied her. I could taste her moods on the air, sense what she hid—suffocation, a longing to be alone. She sat on the couch and read murder mysteries. She ate chocolate, tucked the wrappers into the cushions. She chewed furiously on pecan turtles, never saw how she tossed the house from side to side. On my stomach, I crawled from the kitchen to the living room, watched her turn pages from behind a wingback chair. Her eyes sucked up black type, words like *eviscerate, vivisection, autopsy* pushed out other words—laundry, fold, sweep, mop. Legs crossed in stretch pants, the only thing that moved was her mouth. When she opened it, her teeth were stained with chocolate.

The letters she sends to me in Seattle tell me where her jewelry should go: to my sister, my brother's wife, a grandchild. Her diamond ring, the pearl choker, the jade and turquoise. And then there is the dining-room table that her grandfather Cole built. I used to spin my younger brother on its lazy Susan when we were children. Who should get that? The Persian rugs, the cherry chest of drawers, the maple bedroom suite...

Outside, my father has the girls running through the sprinkler. I go to the window to watch. Nell has grass on her baby-fat face. Angie's clothes are soaked, clinging to her bony frame. She is browning up. In Seattle, the sun is a soft white spot in the clouds. Here in South Carolina, it flares like a tin roof, flashes like glass. It makes the grass sparkle like a body of water.

My mother joins me at the window. Her hair is salt white and sweeps across her forehead. She taps the glass, waves. Angie waves back, squats over the sprinkler letting the spray hit her full on the crotch.

"Good Lord," says my mother, "look at that child. Your father doesn't even notice."

I laugh. "Mama, it's natural." I am always amused when she says *your father.* As if he's mine, not someone she would have anything to do with.

"Mama's planning her funeral again," I say to Ray when the girls and I are back in Seattle. He's on the floor in the kitchen with Angie, teaching her to play the guitar. "She's got me down for the eulogy."

Ray looks up. "I thought she was afraid you'd say something inappropriate."

"Tacky," I say, and sigh. "I guess I've changed." I scoop dough from the bowl where it's been rising, flop it in flour. "I mean, look at me. Baking bread, baking cookies. Helping at Angie's school, picking up trash and dog turd at the park. I'm a fucking model citizen." The dough is whole wheat. Substantial and flabby, like fat at the waist.

Ray laughs, shows Angie how to press her fingers into an A chord. "Don't worry. You're still you."

We live in the Greenwood section of North Seattle. Early risers, we drink the thick coffee I make in a French press, our feet crossed on the deck rail. The sun comes up behind us, turns the dark sky pearly gray. The deck overlooks a backyard with grass, asters, a large oak, and strange purple blossoms that must be weeds.

"How many hours are you working today?" Ray asks.

"Six," I say. "What will you do with the girls?"

"Park, McDonald's," he answers. Angie bangs open the screen door, pads out in her Scooby Doo pajamas. She sits in my lap, thumb in her mouth, sleepy, with the yellow fluffy hair of a chick.

The antique store is busy on Sundays. Couples wander in, drift from the china to rockers with needlepoint seats. My mother calls, back from church. "Can't you get Sundays off?" she asks.

"I'll quit," I say, "when we're done with Ray's school loans." I hang up the phone, turn away from the flat stares of the vintage dolls. They disturb me, these little corpses. The curled eyelashes, rotting dresses. Moth-wing dust on my hands when I touch them. A customer pauses over a floral demitasse, runs her finger around its egg shell bowl, as small and neat as an eye socket. The *bone clean* of bone china.

When I was in South Carolina, my mother showed me the scarlet tailored suit she wants to be buried in. She has saved a tube of the lipstick that matches so I won't have to look for it in the drug store. "Who knows if they'll still make it when I'm dead?" she said. Her suit was zipped into plastic, hanging in the back of her closet. She only wore it once, to have a portrait made. "It's beautiful," she said, "just not practical. Look at this red. Too showy. But good for portraits and lying in state."

I heard the children's voices along with the TV. "Mama," I said, "I've decided to build the coffin myself, in the backyard. The kids can help. It'll be a good family project. Come here and let me measure you."

She batted at me. "Get away. You are not going to measure my behind."

My mother liked us better in the fall, when we were in school. In the summer, she turned us out, our boredom not her responsibility. I'd lie on my back like a swooned princess. The grass pricked sharp and green; the pines put knuckle roots into my bones. From that position, the pines had the look of starved brown arms, fingers spread, open palms holding up the sky.

"Take this to your room, *then come back.*" She stood at the dryer, folding clothes. I was ten and hated her, the livid line of her mouth, her grim tone. The way she threw plates into cabinets as if she hoped they'd break.

At the table, my father and brother talked. Words as thin as ice on a window. We ate the hot food she cooked, while she spooned up frozen chocolate Seago from a can.

"Sell the house," she tells me on the phone. "Split the money four ways, not that you'll get much for it. The neighborhood is in decline."

These days, she's fond of the house, its solid brick walls, and the trees so familiar after all these years. Christmases past were sweeter, the way she watched us from the window, measured us on the door jamb. She gives the house little presents: a remodeled kitchen, new hardwood floors. Like a contrite husband offering his wife the pearl earrings he wishes now he'd given her when her hair was still black and her mouth red.

My mother hung her arm out the window, sang *Camp Town Ladies*, looking like Jackie O in sunglasses that covered most of her face. She pointed the car north on I-95, heading for D.C., the Smithsonian, exotic food, the King Tut exhibit. "Next year," she said, "I'm taking you kids to New York City." Comic books snapped in our hands, folded in half by the wind. A solid wall of trees slid by on either side of the road, telephone wire swooped from pole to pole.

At the theatre, the ballet, the symphony, the air sparked around her. She held our hands to run with us across parking lots. She leaned over to explain stories, sat forward in her seat, squeezed our arms with the rising music.

In our hotel room, she dealt cards on the floor before bedtime. She played hard, as if there were money at stake, but laughed if one us of managed to win. I pressed against her, she rubbed her face against mine, kissed my forehead, nose, cheeks, and chin.

During college, I came home for visits to find new couches, different wallpaper, and the kids' bedrooms shifting into guest rooms and studies. Then Bernadette, folding clothes on our dryer. Bernadette was small, strings of muscles in her brown neck, thin hands that moved swiftly, flipping our clothes back and forth into neat squares. Her shoulder jerked in violent circles as she scrubbed our toilet.

"When did you get her?" I asked as she walked to the end of the driveway to wait for her ride.

"All you kids have learned the value of hard work," my mother said, "now I am damn well going to hire someone else to clean."

Neither she nor my father cooks these days; they "fix food" or go out. They go for weeks to France, Spain, Greece, Russia, China, New Zealand. My mother is friendly and curious. She peers over people's shoulders at lunch counters. Peeks into their bags to see what they have bought. She starts conversations with people who invite her into their homes, cook their food for her. They talk to her in their English, broken or fluent. She tries out their language, her thick Southern accent transforming the words, adding extra vowels.

I met Ray when the court sent me to a clinic for driving drunk. I saw him outside, leather jacket, a thick braid to the middle of his back, and assumed he was a fellow client. Then I walked into the office and found him behind the desk. "Oh shit," I said.

He laughed, gestured at a chair. Said he got taken for a client all the time, especially at the methadone clinic. He bent down to get some papers from a drawer and the braid moved like a snake on his back. I leaned with my arms on his desk, watched him read the questions. *How often do you drink? Do you miss days at work due to drinking?* He made check marks on a page. His lashes were spiky black, his cheekbones high and flat like an Indian's. *Is your mother or father an alcoholic? Do you drink alone?* The questions were so personal, I felt we'd already done things together.

"Do you want to have coffee with me?"

He glanced up, his lips parting in surprise. His throat seemed raw, freshly bruised by a razor.

"Don't say you can't see patients outside the clinic," I said. "I've decided to take the night in jail."

Ray's apartment was on a hill, with a view of the downtown, Mount Rainier on the days it came out of the fog. At night, I sat in a stuffed chair and loosened his braid. He leaned against my knees as I unwound the heavy hair. I pulled it with my hands, worked it with my brush. Thought of looms and weaving. Outside the window, the moon passed under the clouds, rain slipped through the streetlight's circle. Ray's hair fell in black coils and waves, spilled over my lap. I gathered up fistfuls, let my fingers slide through.

I met Ray's father when he and Ray carried a leather couch up the stairs. The father was tall like Ray. He wore a gray mullet and a mustache, his jacket open to expose a narrow frame, white t-shirt stretched over a hard round belly. He'd just been evicted from his apartment. We'd keep his couch, Ray said, until he found another place. The father went down the stairs alone, a bar buddy idling in his pick-up. The pick-up's taillights turned streaks of rain on the window red.

My mother quickly figured out I was living with someone. She gave me two months, then booked a flight to Seattle. I left Ray alone in our apartment, met my mother at the airport. I took her to my friend Janet's house, where we slept together on a lumpy futon.

We met Ray at a Thai restaurant for lunch. My mother had changed into her navy wool suit, her pearl choker. I sat next to her, Ray on the other side of the booth, two gold earrings in one ear, the braid ending in a dark curl between his shoulder blades. We passed Phad Thai, Swimming Angel, and coconut milk soup. My mother chatted easily. Ray told her he'd be in grad school come fall, working on a degree in clinical psychology.

Later, my mother and I made the long drive out to Mount Rainier in the car she'd rented. She was silent, hands at ten and two on the steering wheel. Face blank as she watched the road slide under the car. I sat beside her like someone in a doctor's office. Waiting for test results, hearing myself swallow.

Finally she said, "I don't even know how you would want to do it."

"Do what?"

"Get married."

"Mama," I said, surprised. "Ray and I haven't discussed marriage."

"You're over thirty. Your ovaries aren't getting any younger."

"We haven't discussed children either."

She glanced over her shoulder, whipped the car into the next lane. "My mother just wanted to see me settled before she died," she said. "That's all I want."

Toward the end of my visit, my mother opened the china cabinets in her living room. "There is enough silver for all four of you children," she said. "Just decide who will get what pattern. I'm leaving this up to you because you know what is quality and what is not. Your brothers would sell the Wedgewood for ten cents a piece at an estate sale." She rubbed a spot on her grandmother's goblet. "And make sure you get my gold teeth when I die."

My mother is not dying. She is never sick. Four years ago, a group of Chinese tourists applauded politely when she reached the top step of the Great Wall. "Very good, very strong lady," they said. "How old," they asked, pointing to her white hair.

"Sixty-eight," she said, beaming.

One gentleman bowed, feet together, inclining just his head. "Very beautiful, very strong wife," he told my father.

She baked cookies with my girls. She gave them the twirlers; they licked the pot together. Don't get fat like me, she told them. They grinned at her, chocolate on their teeth and chins. I watched her moving from stove to sink, quick, lithe, efficient. Her face was radiant, open. When I am at her house, I sleep late. I sag on her couch, let her bring me tomato sandwiches from the kitchen.

Later my mother pulled down the stairs and we went up into the attic. The air was hot and unmoving, the corners filled with humped shadows. A Tom Mix rocking horse sat on pink insulation. We stepped from beam to beam. She opened the trunk where her mother's last things were stored. A bed jacket was folded neatly, along with get-well cards, fabrics gently rotting. There was a tray for the years when her mother could still eat, an odd metal instrument, hooked on one end, for the final year. "We used this," she said, "to extract mucus and saliva."

She cut short her first trip to Europe when she got a letter saying her mother had taken a turn for the worse. She was in college then, with flying black hair, crimson lipstick.

"It's not cancer," the doctor told her. "Your mother's tumor is benign. It's the placement in the brain that makes it inoperable."

The tumor grew slowly, luxuriously. It sent out shoots of itself to wind in the brain stem, the spinal cord. It flowered and fruited, pressing here and there, killing circuits one by one. Her mother's legs failed first. She took to a wheelchair. Later she lay in bed, propped on pillows against the headboard. Her right hand curled as it died, fingers drawing inward to the palm.

She washed her mother with warm washcloths, rubbed lotion into her hands, her feet, her face. She uncurled the fingers, cut yellowing fingernails. Her Aunt Rose helped her change the nightgowns, turn the body from side to side. For all the years in bed, her mother never had a bed sore.

In the trunk was a clipboard she used when her mother could no longer speak or hear. On the curled old pages her horrible handwriting was heartrendingly legible. Large, dark, printed letters. *Do you want to sit up? Blink eyes. A visit from Miss Amanda? Blink once for yes.*

I make coffee, Ray strokes my shoulders lightly, brushing over the muscles he knows knot up. He kisses my neck, squeezes the pads of fat on my hips. Our daughters sit on the floor, Angie feeding Nell. She holds Cheerios inches from Nell's mouth, snatching her fingers away as Nell's sharp teeth snap close. Nell laughs with her mouth open wide, spraying out wet bits of cereal. The dryer spins, the refrigerator hums. The glass of the window moves in its frame, as though the house is breathing.

Near the end of my pregnancy with Nell, I was anemic and huge, gassy, my esophagus burning. I drank Milk of Magnesia while Angie, three, grew clingier by the day. "I'm looking forward to that hospital bed," I told my sister on the phone. "I'll sleep. Someone will bring me meals. It'll be like going to a spa."

Ray stayed home with Angie; my mother slept in a chair by my bed. She washed the baby, changed her diapers, clipped her tiny nails. Held her high on her bosom, humming soft show tunes. Their faces touched. "I was never ambivalent about having babies," she remarked. "Babies are wonderful." The nurse had given me pills; the words followed me down into dark water. "It's children who are awful."

"I've been meaning to tell you," my mother said in South Carolina, "should I predecease your father, be sure he signs a prenuptial agreement."

"You think Dad would get married again?" I looked at my father. He was standing in the kitchen, wearing black knee socks with his white shorts. He frowned at a piece of paper in his hand, picked his ear with a Cross pen.

My mother shrugged. "Honey, if I die, there's going to be a line of ladies with casseroles around the block."

My father took the girls to the backyard to play in the sprinkler. My mother and I brought chairs out to watch. The girls ran to me while I was opening my chair. Angie pushed Nell to get there first. My mother scooped up Nell before she could howl, put her between her knees. "Might as well get rid of this." She yanked off the sodden disposable, patted Nell's naked rump. Nell ran back to the sprinkler. "Four kids, cloth diapers," my mother said. "I had my hand in the toilet for seven years."

Angie sprawled in my lap, soaking me with her wet clothes. I examined her nails, chewed to the quick, a crescent of fresh pink blood on one finger. "She didn't used to do this," I said. I saw my mother's hand in the corner of my eye just before she slapped me hard.

"OW!" My head hit Angie's. "What the hell was that for?"

"Mosquito," she said.

I touched my cheek. It stung. "Good Lord, Mama. Next time, let it bite me."

"Sure." She gave me a dazzling smile.

I was drunk once on the New York subway, at three in the morning. I gave a Japanese boy a gold earring because he helped me find the right train home. He didn't want the earring, I pressed it on him. I still have the other one, a thick hoop that belonged to my grandmother. Ray takes his coffee black; I turn mine caramel with cream. Oak leaves curl on our deck; the aster blossoms are so light they float on the slightest of stalks.

We haven't heard from Ray's father in years. He came to the hospital when Angie was born. I slept through his visit. He's never seen Nell. His couch went to Good Will last year, the cushions ripped and patched with duct tape.

We went back to South Carolina to marry before I started showing with Angie. "Ray cleans up good," my mother said. "I figured he would." He had cut his hair, come home with the braid in a box, like a dead pet for me to bury in the back yard.

We bought our house in Greenwood after Ray started at the mental health center. My parents gave us the down payment. From our house, we hear the animals at the zoo. In the morning, the monkeys scream while we drink our coffee. At night, we hear a keeper cough as he shuffles about the snake house, the lioness pant her way through running dreams.

Ray sleeps with his hand on his chest, protecting something. He is clean-shaven now. The bones in his face are clean and strong, the soft skin of the cheeks slowly growing jowls.

Ray comes home at 7:46. The girls run to the door to greet him. "Sorry," he calls to me, as they grab his legs, "meeting ran late." I make him come to me in the kitchen, my hands red and raw, deep in grease and hamburger meat. He approaches cautiously, as if I am a dog that may bite. "How was your day?" Everything I want to say I hold in my mouth, a thousand stinging bees.

He backs out of the kitchen, goes to change out of his suit. Angie snatches at my leg, I drag her over to the stove, slide in the meat, snap the door shut. Nell pulls my arm. The washing machine thumps with another load of clothes and the dust motes spin up, passing through the glass of the window.

It's been years since I've been in a bar. Years since a man sat, listened to me talk, waiting patiently for sex. One man lit my cigarettes across the table, told me he worked in construction with his brother. I told him about the trip to Italy with my sister. Pompeii, I told him, was a weird graveyard. There were ovens on the streets, inside the bread had turned to stone. In the Garden of the Fugitives, there were plaster casts of thirteen bodies laid together like the bodies at Jonestown. Children curved toward their mothers, one man balanced on his elbow. My sister tried to nudge me on to the brothel. I ignored her, squatted to peer into black hole eyes, at lips pulled open by cinder and dust. I counted eyelashes, traced the lines of eyelids and fingernails. The man lit my cigarette, his face blank and orange in the flare. It was still there, I told him. Still intact. The patterns of hair, the lines of lashes and lids. Curled into the palms, fingerprints. Still there, the fine lines of self.

In South Carolina, my mother drove the car. When we stopped for gas, she hopped out to do the pumping herself. I was vaguely embarrassed; she is past seventy after all. Back on the road, she got on to the topic of a tasteful headstone. "I might go ahead and have it made myself," she said, "and you can fill in the date later."

"Forget it," I said. "I've already commissioned a winged marble goddess."

I dropped her at Aunt Rose's. I stayed a while so Aunt Rose could see the kids. Angie found an open bag of chocolate chips in with the canned peaches. She shoved chips into her mouth, hid under the kitchen table until I dragged her out by one foot. She screamed, her hands flying at me until I pinned her in my arms. Nell sat on Aunt Rose's lap, stroking the puckers of skin on her neck. Finally I buckled the kids back in their car seats, began the drive on to North Carolina to see a girlfriend.

The twilight came and the girls fell asleep. I was submerged in quiet with the things that roll in the undercurrent. What would I do with Mama's gold teeth anyway? Melt them down to make earrings? What did my Japanese boy do with his gold earring, his piece of a stranger's past? What will I say at the front of the church to the congregation, to ladies with casseroles baked, dreaming of becoming my father's next wife? Ray sleeps with his hand covering his heart and Mama and I meet every year in New York. We used to go to the top of the Twin Towers and stand with our toes against the windows. We put our noses against the glass and the building disappeared. It was like standing in the sky above in the city.

At the end of my visit to South Carolina, my mother drove me to the airport to fly back to Seattle. After a month, I was ready to go home, back to my husband, my routines, the antique store. She walked us to the baggage scanners and my daughters and I passed through, leaving her on the other side. The bittersweet filled and filled me until I was one turn away from vomiting it all out: muscle and bone and blood, all the strings and knots that hold me together. I waved goodbye, seeing her in her red suit, flying in the air, like a woman in a Chagall painting. My daughters laughed and waved, throwing out kisses that my mother pretended to catch, spread on her cheeks or tuck into her pockets. She plucked a kiss out of the air, impishly dropped it down her bosom. My girls shrieked and threw more kisses. She caught one, planted it on her rear. I laughed and waited, holding it in my hand, the shape of what it will be like, finally, never to see her again. ༄

Anniversary

Judy Katz

Everywhere I look I see you.
April again. The coffee sitting too long
in its white cup leaves a ring the color of your straw hat,
the one you wore in the garden. In forsythia, I see you.
The small diamond chip in a stranger's ear.
On the bus I see you, and in galleries and cafes.
Your red coat. I see you young and I see you old.
Imagine, I see you old! Illumined by white hair, you are
drinking juice. I see you in paintbrushes and water towers.
On evening walks, in the broken sky
between buildings, I piece you
together.

It is Passover again.
I see you at the *seder*, your pink and white robe,
in sweet apples and salt water, in the blunt, bitter root.
Tell me, exactly when is the moment
of passing?

I travel to the desert, and there you are—
the low airport buildings are yours; the sudden mountains,
yours. The clear light, the thin air, the fifty
shades of green beside the road. At midday,
the rutted hills are your hands. We drive
and I see them all day long.

I see you as you were, and as you never were.
In charcoal and in flesh, with the unrelenting mind
of Spring, I see you. The petal of the crocus
that clings to my finger, the purple capillaries
sprouting in my leg. You are the pavement,
the bucket of daffodils the grocer moves
to the front window.

ॐ

The Weight of Absence

Judy Katz

When you died our house sank deeper into the earth,
pressing on the roots of trees.
I could feel it sinking
as each visitor pushed open the front door,
laden with cakes and casseroles, the full weight
of their bodies—every muscle and tendon,
shinbone   pelvis   hips   moving
down the hallway, moving past the closet
where your dresses hung, still with your smell,
moving into the living room where our father
sat low to the ground.

I had watched you grow smaller and smaller,
ice chips on your tongue.
And as the morphine took you
here and there, Paris and summer camp,
the lake at night—
I thought I understood:
lighter and lighter
you would become,
a lightness leading
to nothing.

But the house did not rise that day;
it sank.
No mass   no matter
no thing   in the bed
in the blankets
in your place.

ဆ

Lunch at My Late Mother's, Improvised

Elizabeth Biller Chapman

We've been tasting dust: closet, drawer,
an attic fan roused, not much help, and grumbling.
Those gray and white plates of every day,
and the party bowls, packed and shipped.
My sisters having gone, another round is over.
                    Everything I chose was chipped.

Clinging to the same thread, five of us here—
old friends, her housekeeper, my first-born, grown—
find unexpired tuna, cucumber, light
and dark swirl pumpernickel bread.
We set a table in the open air.
                   No one's right in that corner

where she sat once, opposite the 40's bassinet
like an airy cage on legs—white high heels—
a sleeveless and striped summer dress. Now
knifed cantaloupe, a chocolate cake perhaps not quite
defrosted. I struggle with the ice trays.
                 "These chairs'll last forever,"

Mr. Butts said, brooming the garage. Some long-
forgotten daylilies stretch across the lawn. Breath
of the garden, my father's work always:
this wide porch, close as she got to it.
I let my sternum rise and fall;
               rise and fall for her

rising and falling. Once, profusion in the far beds:
yellow, orange, red tomatoes, baby pear
and little plum, their unique musk. All
those firefly summers when we'd rush to eat
as much as we could hold
                 direct from the vine.

      ଔ

Nesting in a Season of Light

Angela Wheelock

Spring in the Yukon is all edges and sharp light, with ice-choked rivers running to join the sea. After the vernal equinox, the days steadily lengthen, and by May, it is light when you go to bed at night, and light when you get up in the morning. Some people put aluminum foil over their bedroom windows, but I never did. I liked to go to sleep with the afterglow of sunset lingering in the shadows; I always felt hopeful then. Maybe that's why I was sure that May would be the month that I would get pregnant. Even though we had already lost one pregnancy, we still had the innocence of those who don't truly understand how things can go wrong.

May is called 'Eggs Month' by the Kaska because that is when birds lay their eggs and the land returns to life after winter darkness. Kaska, northern relatives of the Navajo, live in a handful of villages in the Yukon. My husband Pat and I had lived in the northernmost of these villages, Ross River, for five years the spring we were determined to have a baby.

A terraced hill looms over the village. You can hike to the top of this hill and look down to where Ross River lies at the confluence of the Pelly and Ross Rivers. Down below are the older log cabins and the newer pre-fab houses of the native village and the modest brown house where we lived. You can make the houses disappear by lifting two fingers and holding them in front of your face as you look down. It will seem as though there are no people living in that country; all you will see are mountains and trees and rivers shining in the sun.

"It is important that any woman planning to get pregnant have a good knowledge of her body's cycles," the fertility book I was reading informed me.

By spring, I had given up recording my basal temperature, after never observing any clear patterns. Instead, we relied on having sex every two days during the most likely time of month. By Mother's Day, my period was late—the kind of late that only someone obsessed with becoming pregnant would even notice. On day eight of my missed period, I felt brave enough to expose my tender hope to the scrutiny of a pregnancy test. When I arrived at the nursing station, the nurse, Babs from Ontario, was sitting outside drinking a glass of orange juice, yawning.

"It's the light," she said. "I can't sleep."

I peed into a cup and waited nervously, sitting on a stool in one of the examining rooms, as Babs held the test strip in her hand.

"It looks like it's turning positive," she said with a smile.

On the weekend, we worked up space for a garden. Pat spaded horse manure into the dark soil and I organized the plants and seeds. The soil looked rich, but it wouldn't grow anything without fertilizer.

"If insufficient progesterone is being produced in the second half of the menstrual cycle, the endometrial lining will not thicken and develop enough to support the embryo," I read. I knew that I had a hormonal imbalance. Our doctor, whom I will call Doctor Brown, loved to talk about what this might mean. For now, we were doing very little—not intervening, as Doctor Brown said.

Pat went away for a week, not long after we saw Dr. Brown. I was angry even though, as he pointed out, there was nothing he could do to control the outcome of the pregnancy. I took comfort in hanging clothes on the line that stretched across our yard. As the song of a Swainson's thrush drifted over from the nearby woods, I fitted wooden clothespins to damp T-shirts and pants and socks. In the afternoon, I buried my face in armloads of cotton, inhaling the scent of clothes dried in the open air.

In the early days of June, I began spotting. When I called Dr. Brown, I asked about the possibility of progesterone and he explained that in order for progesterone to work, I should have begun taking it before conception. Dr. Brown lived in Whitehorse, a five-hour drive from Ross River, by way of a narrow gravel road that winds up over heights, then dips down to creeks, skirting muskeg and mountains. With this journey in mind, we decided to stay in Ross and take our chances with the visiting doctor who examined me and reluctantly agreed to phone in a prescription for progesterone. Much later, I learned that a pelvic exam was exactly the wrong thing to do. But that was later. As we left the nursing station, I held onto my body and moved slowly, stepping up into our truck without saying anything.

The next morning, the fragile pregnancy fell out of my body. Dr. Brown had asked us to save anything we could in the event of a miscarriage, so Pat placed the small bit of blood and tissue into a clean glass jar as I wept.

The light, which was nearing its peak as the summer solstice approached, took away some of my grief. A week later, when light was filling the world, we transplanted wildflowers from the roadside to our yard. We dug up clumps of shrubby beard's tongue, a blue-blossomed member of the penstemon family that grows on bare hills. Flowers are like that in the Yukon, growing in the

merest hint of soil. Hunkered low to the ground, they defy the subarctic climate;
I didn't feel nearly as sturdy.

On the first weekend in July, we hiked up into the alpine in an area frequented
by small herds of woodland caribou. We surprised one herd in a snow patch and
the caribou galloped away from us, their strong legs carrying them effortlessly
over the next ridge. I, on the other hand, was hesitant as I hiked, not yet
recovered from the miscarriage.

As I look back, it seems as if that summer was filled with sadness. One
day, however, as I was riffling through a shoebox of snapshots, I found a
photograph taken that summer of my mother and me. I'm wearing a fuschia
shirt and clutching a bouquet of flowers; we're both smiling. "Wasn't that a good
visit," my mother scrawled on the back of the picture. I have little memory of
that visit, but I do remember that in August we were full of renewed optimism.
We were going to meet again with Dr. Brown and develop a new strategy.
Things would work out.

In August, chinook salmon arrive in the Lapie River and other tributaries of
the Pelly, having traveled thousands of miles upstream from the mouth of the
Yukon. They follow the scent of home until they come to the place where they
were born. There the females lay eggs and the males fertilize them. Then, spent
by their marathon journey, the fish die. Biology exerts a strong pull. We decided,
that August, that I would begin taking Clomid.

"Clomiphene citrate has been successfully used for many years to stimulate
women to ovulate," my fertility book explained.

"But I ovulate don't I?" I asked. "Otherwise, how could I get pregnant?"

"Actually," Dr. Brown said, "it is possible to sort of ovulate."

Apparently a woman can ovulate in such a way that things won't work out.
Maybe, he said, that was what was wrong with me.

In September, bull moose run headlong through willow thickets and
buckbrush, maddened with the desire to mate. Pat and I hadn't reached the
point-of-panic yet, but sometimes I felt panic's breath on the back of my neck
and heard it whispering words in my ear: childless, barren, hopeless. We had sex
whether we were in the mood or not. Afterwards, I lay still until the wet spot
beneath me began to cool. Then I put on my pajamas and thought about how
I might already be pregnant, even though it would be at least two weeks until I
could risk a pregnancy test.

In the autumn mornings, the grass in our yard was coated in a sheath of frost. In
the afternoons, sandhill cranes rode the thermals over the hill and wheeled and

circled, their voices a distant clamor carried on the wind. The last of the aspen leaves clung to the trees—rustling.

In early October, we learned that I was pregnant and, for a brief moment, we were wildly happy. Dr. Brown was guardedly hopeful. By the third week of the pregnancy, I was again spotting. Spotting, I learned, was a euphemism for bleeding that was particularly cruel in its ambiguity: it might be ominous or it might be meaningless. The only way to know would be whether the pregnancy continued or it didn't.

Soon, snow blanketed the ground and the house boomed and cracked as the falling temperatures caused the walls to contract. We had done everything that Dr. Brown recommended and it wasn't enough; this pregnancy seemed as doomed as all the rest. In mid-November, we went to Whitehorse for an ultrasound. The technician had little to say during the test, but his face told us that it wasn't good news. We had to wait, he said, for Dr. Brown.

"Your uterus is empty," Dr. Brown said softly.

His theory was that I had had another miscarriage, and he seemed nearly as sad as we were with this latest setback. Two days later, after a D & C to clean the remnants out of my uterus, we were on our way back to Ross River, unaware that my body was a ticking time bomb.

Unbeknownst to us or to the ultrasound machine, one of my eggs had gotten caught in the narrow tunnel of my left fallopian tube and implanted itself there after fertilization. All the time that I thought I was recovering from another miscarriage, a trapped embryo was growing. It grew until in the early hours of the morning—four days after the D & C—the ectopic pregnancy ruptured, causing massive internal bleeding.

Somehow I managed to sleep through this life-threatening event. But when I arose, I fell back onto the bed gasping, unable to stand.

I screamed.

On any other morning I would have died right there on the bed or somewhere on the way to the kitchen, where the only phone hung on the wall too high for someone crawling to reach. But this morning, Pat was late leaving for work and heard my scream. When Henry, the local nurse, arrived and took my blood pressure, the lower number was close to zero.

At the local nursing station, I was put on electrolytes and oxygen to keep my body functioning until a plane arrived to medivac me to the hospital in Whitehorse. Meanwhile, the bleeding continued and I fought to push the oxygen mask off my face.

"I'm dying, aren't I?" I asked Henry.

"We haven't lost anyone yet," Henry answered, as sweat poured off his face.

I was carried onto the plane nearly five hours after first awakening that morning. Dr. Brown was the first person I saw in Whitehorse.

"We're going to operate," he said. "Do you understand?"

I managed to shake my head yes. It was the last thing I remembered until I awoke in the recovery room, woozy from anesthesia and blood loss. Dr. Brown explained that I only had one remaining fallopian tube and that most of the blood in my body was no longer my own. Because he had missed the ectopic pregnancy on the ultrasound, I needed emergency surgery. Because he was an excellent surgeon, he saved my life. It would be a long time, however, before I had enough strength to think about this. Meanwhile, the nurses admired the stitches on my belly and injected me with morphine.

"Don't mind the fetal pig," my sister had said to me years earlier, when I opened her refrigerator to get some cream for my coffee.

Sure enough, there was a fetal pig covered with saran wrap nestled between the milk and the orange juice—homework for biology. As I lay in the hospital bed, I remembered that pig and I envied my sister the sight of intestines, heart, lungs. I wished then that my abdomen was a permeable membrane and that I could insert my hand and fix what had gone wrong.

The second day after my surgery, I stood in the dingy shower stall weeping with rage as water ran over my body. Despite the fact that I had lost two previous pregnancies, I still believed that Doctor Brown had the answers. Now, all of that had fallen away.

As the year wound down, snow fell from a gray sky—snow on snow on snow. The days were so short that I could feel the dark pressing at the back of my eyes. After New Year's, I sat for hours in the oak rocking chair that nestled beside the woodstove, looking out the front window over the mountains. I found out that grief isn't like anything you imagine. It isn't really like sadness; it is more like feeling you're going crazy.

"Make a list," the counselor I met in the hospital advised me when I found the strength to phone her. "It doesn't matter what's on it. It will give you something to focus on."

My list contained the barest elements of functioning: get out of bed, make coffee, brush hair. Most days though, I ignored my list and sat and turned the details of the ectopic pregnancy over and over in my mind, until the memories were polished as smooth as the stones you find near rushing rivers. I didn't want to see people or talk to anyone.

"Light griefs can speak; great ones are dumb," Seneca wrote nearly two millennia ago. I think he was right.

Pat expressed his grief differently. His axe connected with frozen blocks of wood in the back alley. One piece of wood became three, again and again, until there was a pile of wood ready to be carried into the house. At night, I lay awake listening to the wood in the stove talking, as the water burned out of it, wishing that I could deal with my sorrow in such a physical way.

In mid-February, we traveled to Watson Lake, a round trip of about five hundred miles. As daylight faded, we climbed the continental divide, and ptarmigan flew up from the margin of the road like ghost birds in the dusk. At nearby Frances Lake, a thin yearling moose was standing beside the road, snow falling onto its back. The yearling ran as we came closer, plowing through deep snow. Our headlights illuminated the tracks where its mother had run off. We stopped to watch for a moment with the windows rolled down and we could see the moose's breath coming in puffs of white against the gray of twilight.

Over the days and weeks that followed, the image of that young moose alone in the semi-darkness kept returning to my mind; a key fitted into a door I hadn't realized I needed to open. What was it, I wondered, about that young moose and the fact that his mother had run off into the growing darkness that kept inserting itself into my thoughts?

At another visit to Frances Lake, we discovered chewed moose bones—the remains of a wolf kill. Moose are notoriously fierce in the defense of their young—kicking out in a flash of leg and hoof. Wolves respect this fierceness, but succeed in killing yearlings nonetheless. Acknowledging that desire cannot always affect outcome—whether one is a human mother or a moose—drove a wedge of solace into my grief. For the first time, I thought about what it might mean to forgive myself, and the baby I will never know, for the intersection of events that took its life and almost cost me mine.

One night in March, I walked home from a meeting under a mostly clear sky. The moon poked out from behind a cloud and the northern lights licked at the top of the hill, and in the intake of a breath the aurora drew closer, filling the sky with shimmering light. It occurred to me then, that although isolated from the urban phenomenon of support groups during the ebb and flow of conception and loss, I didn't lack support. Starlight and daylight, raven and thrush, had been my companions on the journey. They could not speak words of comfort, but that was not a shortcoming. They say that listening is the greatest gift we can offer to one who grieves; the Yukon wilderness holds an infinity of listening.

In April, we talked about trying to get pregnant again. The one thing we were sure of was that Ross no longer felt like a safe place. On weekends, we looked at houses in Whitehorse. Back in Ross, the signs of spring seemed more poignant, with the awareness that it would be our last. Spring comes to Whitehorse too, but it is a different place. In the evenings, we picked wild crocus, whose blooms cast a purple haze over the bare hillsides. Plants leapt out of the ground, growing quickly in the cool air and long light of spring days.

Flocks of lapland longspurs roamed through the village, eating seeds at the edges of fields and lawns. When I looked up from something else, I caught a glimpse of a flock wheeling across the sky. The small birds sounded like miniature chimes turning together in the wind. My Audubon field guide told me that they are "bold in the breeding territories." Soon, they would be on the tundra. They would follow the light out to the edge of the land where the trees end and the Arctic Ocean begins. Once I found an injured lapland longspur, in the grass near the store. When I picked it up and cupped it in my hands, I felt the fierce drumming of its heart. I thought about that fierceness as I watched these spring birds eating, preparing for nesting in a season of light. &

Baby

Lois Taylor

There's no going back. The bruised shadows of the Rockies swallow the train as surely as the tunnels. The train itself is plush, with polished fittings, and colored redcaps. It's bound for New Denver.

Ruthie is miscarrying. Half of her is relieved, but the other half is terrified. She's dignified yet maidenly at thirty, with her mother's narrow feet but none of her daintiness, and at five-foot-nine, towered over everyone in school photographs.

She made the traveling suit herself. She's been poor all her life so this is nothing remarkable. Her sisters married poor men, too. Only their father even dreams of rich husbands.

She's been told she cuts an elegant figure, and this she believes. She just doesn't believe it makes her someone to be petted or treasured. Somebody's baby.

The pains deepen. She grips the windowsill, then stands and rushes down the aisle to the lavatory, the baby slung on her hip in desperation.

Once there with the door closed, she props the baby on the sink and lets her play with the taps. Pieces of liver come. Now Ruth sees blood beat behind her lids in spasms. She is alone and dying. In her heart of hearts she had doubts about another child, and now she must pay.

Meanwhile, Hugh plays cards in New Denver with the town doctor, also the town lush. It's a long wait for Ruthie's train, and he feels like celebrating. He has his first job since almost going to prison for stealing money from the last.

Ruthie found the money in an empty cocoa tin. He refused to answer her questions. She called him a castout from the prairie and not one of his family worth a lick. He said, "Lace curtain Irish, la di da. Your father's no better! A boilermaker, or would be if he could get on!" Hugh knows her father is a good man, and fears his own nature has come down to him like a curse, father to son.

"Don't you *dare* speak against him," Ruthie said. "You're not fit to clean his boots."

The baby began to cry then, and Hugh stormed out. It was a low moment. But now he's found work. A fresh start in the mountains. She helped him pack, and straightened his cowlick with a smile.

He can change. He will be better and never hit again, no, never.

Hugh's job is stringing the first telephone wires across inland British Columbia. The doc shares an interest in drinking and cards. He's heard talk about the doc and his nurse, Helene, though the doc is married with six kids.

Now the doc is dealing a new hand.

Hugh slips the cards together by suit, thinking about the cabin on Winnow Lake he got for a song. The former occupant had climbed a cedar near the front steps, and jumped from a branch with a noose around his neck. He left no note, no family, and no story that anyone knew. They buried him in the small cemetery with a stake in the ground, should anyone arrive later to ask what became of him.

He wonders whether to tell Ruthie about this. It's the kind of thing women can be funny about.

Hugh stares at the full house in his hand, thinking about Helene. A flirt and no doubt about it. When he speculates about her or any other woman, he feels a stubborn place inside, no bigger than a knuckle, but immovable.

He met Ruthie at a dance. A stranger had grabbed Hugh by the scruff of the neck after some bitter words. This was something the old man had done when Hugh was a boy, living in his house, eating his bread. A fight broke out, people cheering and whistling. Ruthie was drawn to the racket.

Hugh counts his winnings now, while the doc deals. He'll keep them in a lockbox in the cabin's attic. Ruthie won't go up there; she's terrified of bats.

He touches his new moustache. He thinks of his mouth as small and mean. His teeth aren't good either, the prairie with its poor water and poorer diet. He already has laugh trenches on his face, and scars from smallpox; but when his cowlick pops up, or his hair falls on his forehead, Ruthie tells him he looks like a boy. He doesn't hold a grudge, except for his father, but that's another matter. Ruthie nurses a grudge; her anger blows, fades, blows again undiminished. He'll never understand it.

Ruthie gives the baby her necklace to play with and she puts the beads immediately in her mouth. In New Denver, Ruth will rub whisky on the baby's gums to help her sleep. But for now, the cool slippery beads.

There's a knock at the door. Ruthie's flooding now, her life leaving like warm sand. She believes that soon she will faint away and die. But the loss of blood makes her less desperate. This is so clearly something she can't do a thing about.

She pants, "Yes?" She can't remember if she locked the door.

The door opens an inch. A soft male voice says, "Ma'am? You all right in there?"

She tries to stand but her legs won't hold her. She's afraid to look down at what she's passing.

The door opens another inch, then, slowly, all the way.

A colored redcap stands in it. Lord have mercy, he says, and steps in.

He lifts the child. Thinking of that old song about trouble at the door, he closes it behind him. He has to keep this job. No work in Detroit; he couldn't even get on with the trains there. Then word came that Canadian Pacific needed porters, Canadian or not don't matter. He feels like the only black man in the world some days, though there are East Indians and Chinamen on the streets of Vancouver. Coloreds, just not his color. His father said the further north you go, the whiter they get.

He carries the child, who is sucking on pretend pearls, out into the hallway, and down the aisle to the cupboards, to get towels.

When he comes back, the lady is curled on the floor, blood everywhere. He thinks of butchering day on the farm, before they moved up north.

He reaches over her to flush, and closes the lid. She's shaking like a leaf on a tree. He sets the child on the sink and lifts the shaking woman to the commode. She moans.

He hands her a towel and drops others onto the floor, then taps and spreads them with his foot.

"Can you stand, little lady?" he asks the child. "Cause Lemuel's about to set you on your pins." She stares at him. The woman says, "She's a year; she can walk."

People smile as they go down the aisle again. Coloreds are good with children, aren't they, like children themselves.

He returns with a blanket, and remembers now where he's seen this. Not butchering day. It was in Detroit. Daddy and all six brothers headed for church, and Mama stayed home. When they got back, she was groaning in bed and they peeked and saw bloody rags in a basin. He was full-grown before he understood that she'd got rid of number seven.

He closes the door and the child stands inside it, sucking on a pearl necklace. He hands the blanket to the lady. She's pale as a sack of flour.

"Thank you." She takes the blanket from the redcap and wraps it around her shoulders.

It's a miracle, she thinks, the skirt isn't ruined. First time on my body, it'd be such a waste. It's flecked with blood, but as she likes to say of a run in her stockings: if you walk fast, nobody'll notice. She does feel better, she does, she's sure of it. The blood is less. Something dying inside—terrible, but can't dwell on it. "I think I'm a little better. Yes, I am," she tells the redcap as he rinses the sink.

She's thinking of Hugh, now that she's going to live. Is there a Gladys or Betty already? Those were the ones she knew of. Means nothing, he said. How could he say that? It meant everything. Those vows and the ring, everything.

"Help me up, can you?" she says. "I have to get up now."

The redcap turns and reaches a hand. She pauses, staring, then takes it.

He lifts her to her feet. Her hands hold on tight, and she comes up slow.

She's tall as Mama before she shrunk, but this lady is *skinny*. And white as wash. He sees her stockings have drops of blood. Her legs wobble. He lowers her to the commode again.

Behind him, the child begins to whimper. "Little lady, you need to stop whimpering." He sets her back on the sink. She reaches for his cap and kicks her white boots. She's dropped the necklace. He hands it to her and turns to wipe blood from the stockings.

"I think it's over," she says. "It is, it's over." It stopped. Turned off like a faucet. Her skin is warm again. She sobs once, in relief. Underwear in her luggage back at their seat. Everything will be fine.

He says, "I'm going to find someone for the little lady till you're up to it."

She describes a valise she wants, and while she talks, he takes in the homemade suit, the cloth bag. This is not a rich woman, traveling out of pleasure and idleness.

He knows how to tell white people, and walks the child down the aisle until he sees one with a kind face, nice clothes, and above her on the rack, good luggage. Tells her he's sorry to disturb, but this little lady's mama has been overcome with an attack against her health, could she take the child for a few minutes?

The woman says he is a good Samaritan. He says, Just part of the job, ma'am. Well it is not!, she says, getting worked up a little, so he simply hands the child to her.

The tiny room's quiet with them gone, and smells like tin. She sponges off the suit. Much better, much, though in the mirror she's the color of tallow.

What to do with the kind redcap? If she gives him money, there might not be enough for supper, and Nanny's sandwiches and the peach are gone. The baby's milk is in bottles and she can eat mashed potatoes and other soft foods. But if you don't tip, it looks mean.

A knock. She says, "Come." He has such nice manners, she's made such a mess.

He carries rags, a bucket and mop, and the small brown vanity case. A man passing tries to peer in, but he squeezes himself and the bucket through the door, and closes it behind.

"I don't know how to thank you." She pulls up her feet and watches him squeeze rags into the bucket, then mop the floor. So dark and strange. Her father, a Socialist despite daydreams of wealth, calls them Negroes.

She's alive, and the baby is somewhere else, just for now. Her shoes look fine. Bought with her first paycheck from the Rose Rest Home, where she briefly worked after she took the baby and left. Nanny and Pop watched the baby and off she went every day, happy as a lark. Pop called her Tillie the Toiler. But then Hughie came, and he was so sorry, and he'd found a job that paid better than hers. So proud and sorry. *A marriage is a marriage,* people said.

She watches the redcap wring his mop. Stuttering, but determined, she says she feels bad about all he's done, but is short of cash just now.

He turns to her. The whites of his eyes are yellow-white, and the centers black. She's never seen someone so dark up close. He pushes the air to show he wouldn't think of taking her money. The pinkness of his palms is somehow embarrassing.

The lavatory is almost normal now. The redcap returns carrying a tray with water and a cup of tea.

She says, "Thank you" again, and drinks the water straight down. She could die of thirst.

She thought this one was a boy. Her throat catches as she swallows, but you can drown in regret as surely as water if you let yourself.

Hugh curls up on the doc's snooze cot while the doctor slumps in a chair, snoring. The room smells of booze and peanuts. The other card players have gone home.

He's thinking of Helene, the doc's redhead nurse. She'd light up a room if you ever got her clothes off.

Men don't wolf-whistle when Ruthie passes, but that's because she looks like she'd knock your hat off for you. She was sickly way back, when she was little. Just after the Spanish Influenza. People put flags out when someone was sick, then a black one for death. She had rickets, and her rib cage didn't grow, her secret shame. Only the one breast, the other never developed.

He tells her it doesn't matter, but when they're smoking afterward, he imagines her with both. Need clouds your eyes, and when it's gone, you see what you've got.

In less than a year, there'll be another baby. His own family averaged a child a year, until Harry. Harry was the one the old man's eyes fell on when he came home mean and drunk. He stood out in some way. They said Harry hurt himself and died from falling on ice, but the old man cracked Harry's skull. You could hear it clear across the room.

Hugh left the prairie and never went back, not even for their mother's funeral. She never could protect them. She only made the old man madder.

He vows to think of his dead brother more often. He drowses on the doc's snooze cot, aware of dreaming, but unable to recollect them when he wakens.

Ruthie orders carefully. A salad with tomatoes and cottage cheese and a bright red cherry on top. White bread and butter for the baby, sprinkled with sugar despite a sour look from the old bat across the aisle.

She looks out the window, enjoying the trip for the first time. A while ago, a murmur travelled down the dining car. Someone had spotted a mountain goat family. She's too exhausted to get wrought up about mountain goats.

She holds her head high as she walks the baby back to the seat. The child is perfect. She's hoping not to bump into the redcap. His kindness was both miraculous and embarrassing.

The baby gives into a nap with no fussing. Another miracle. She watches her lids twitch. What do babies dream? A year ago there was no such person. She thinks of pieces left behind on the tracks like breadcrumbs. No more babies. That's one thing she knows for sure now. When she ponders families up and down the block, it seems clear that children cause poverty. Pain is endurable but poverty turns you into a heap of salt. Not every one can make it into this world, and once here, it's a mixed blessing.

The conductor announces New Denver in twenty minutes. Hughie's letter said it was a pretty little town, but rough at the edges. He'll be at the station with his new doctor-friend. A strange coincidence, though she believes the worst is over now and she'll have no need of doctors.

Hugh will be gone for long stretches. She'll heat water on the coal-and-wood range to carry to nickel tubs, and scrub on a washboard. It'll be hard, but she's done it before. What grows where winter is nine months long? A garden civilizes a place. Green beans and squash.

Surely there aren't many unmarried women so far from the city. She's not afraid of the cabin, or of being alone, of anything, except their new life collapsing under the weight of hope.

The first thing she sees is the moustache. What does he think he's doing! A bleak waiting room slowly passes, the sign announcing New Denver, a cluster of people.

Hands behind his back like a skater, he peers into window after window. Then he sees her face, and runs along the train with his hand on its side, cowlick wafting.

She shakes her head as if she can't believe her eyes. Snow on the ground and him with no hat. Such a headlong, darling man.

He rocks his arms, and she points to the seat where the baby sleeps. The train slows. She sits down with her heart in her throat. Everything has brought them to this place.

Nights will be long in the mountains, the winter white and still. Everything she plants will be cropped to the root by starving deer. She'll see the hanging man out of the corner of her eye as she carries laundry to the clothesline.

She steps onto the platform.

A strange woman pops out from behind the men. She dips in a curtsy that feels like a slap.

"Welcome to New Denver," she giggles. "Helene." Extends her left hand, a camera in her right.

They line up obedient as cattle for the picture, Ruthie and Hugh flanking the doctor, who holds the baby.

The woman raises the camera to her eye and cries, "Hughie! Smile as if you owe me money."

The mountains are in the background. Except for Ruthie, everyone in the photograph is looking away. Hugh, with his head thrown back and eyes squeezed shut, is laughing. The doctor bends to the baby, her white face a thumbprint. Only Ruthie stares out at the photographer. ❧

Silence Manager

Eugenia Chao

It was a stroke of genius that our 10th grade class teacher, Mrs. Yang, appointed Tong as the new Silence Manager. Ours was far from an obedient or silent class—in fact, we were notorious for fights and noise and disturbances of multitudinous sorts. Since Mrs. Hwaun—the class teacher assigned to us for our first year at Ho Ping Junior High—had passed away, all the transfer students and problem teens kicked out of other classes ended up in our classroom. I wasn't a gangster girl or anything, but my best friend Mei Su "knew some people." In my loyalty to her, I found myself in a number of problem situations, and eventually, in this class.

This was Taipei, and one doesn't think of the capital of Taiwan without getting the dark image of gangsters in one's mind. Tong was the protégée of a gangster group outside of school and, aside from being popular, athletic, and a D student, he was absolutely gorgeous. His face was a delicate acorn shape, the translucency of his skin almost feminine, infantile, in its beauty. His eyelashes were long and dense and dark, almost unnatural, like fake eyelashes. Tong wasn't especially tall, but tall enough, slender from playing basketball three hours a day. He always wore the finest name-brand sneakers, and, tied around his neck with a piece of red string, a piece of sparkling green jade given to him by his mother.

Tong and his friends had always been the main source of noise in our classroom. They were raucous, hooting loudly at any opportunity. During the baseball season, all the boys huddled around the tiny class television set, following the scores, screaming and cursing at the diminutive green- and yellow-clad players on the screen. Tong and his friends, who supported the "Brothers" team, banged yellow acrylic cones on wooden desks to egg their team on. This would provoke the supporters of the green United team.

"F--- you yellow suckers, your team is no good and they look retarded in striped pants, like skinny clowns. Ugly stinky turtles."

"What did you say? I dare you to say that again. Your green team is the one who's going to get it bad!"

Then they would bang their yellow and green cones against each other and the walls and bookshelves, exchanging obscenities. About this point, one of our high school's discipline officers or our class teachers would storm in and tell them to put a lid on it, or they'd line up all the boys at the discipline office in the basement to receive demerits, which would remain on their records and brand them for the rest of their lives.

Now, all of a sudden, Tong was the Silence Manager of our class. Normally the committee of student managers and staff in the classroom was comprised of A students, teachers' pets, and other responsible individuals. Tong was five hundred miles away from any of those categories.

One day, Tong stood in front of the classroom, looking at us, and all of a sudden a joking monkey-grin appeared on his face. Our teacher, Mrs. Yang, was gone for the afternoon.

"Now everybody, be quiet—be *good,*" Tong said.

His friends snickered and the rest of the class squirmed uncomfortably in their seats, wondering what Mrs. Yang had been thinking when she put the king prankster in charge of the rest of us. With three pieces of chalk held together in his left hand, Tong began to carve the characters for silence, *an zin*. Every few strokes, he deliberately dropped a piece of chalk and let it break into little pieces on the floor.

"Butterfinger," someone called out.

"What's the matter, Tong? Got a hole in your hand?" another boy said. "Man, I wish I had a hole in my hand too, that would feel *sooo* good when I'm alone in my room."

By the time Tong had finished writing *an zin* in crooked script on the board, he had used up all the white chalk and his friends were hugging their stomachs from laughing so hard. A couple of the other students giggled, too, but their muffled laughs were reserved and nervous. The Silence Manager then opened the drawer of the lectern and pulled out our class teacher's formidable bamboo stick. He beat the lectern twice with the tip of the weapon and everyone snapped to attention. He pointed at the blackboard and enunciated as if speaking to second graders.

"Re-peat after me," he said. "*Aaaan zziiin.*"

People started giggling at this, while some of Tong's friends imitated him, pretending to mispronounce and stumble over the words.

"*A-an chin.*"

Tong beat the board with the bamboo stick and spoke in a fake hysterical woman's voice. "Now *an zin*! Shut the fuck up all of you. If I hear a peep out of any single one of you little people, my Big Brothers and I will be waiting for you outside the front gate today."

The class was dead silent for five minutes until our math teacher walked in. Tong bowed to her and let her have the space in the front of the classroom as well as the bamboo stick. She smiled, surprised and obviously impressed.

"So you have a new Silence Manager, I see," she said. "Excellent job, Tong. If only you could be as good about handing in your math homework."

Tong's friends poked and patted him on his sides and back. He beamed, proud of being a successful tyrannical Silence Manager as well as someone who never handed in homework. Neglecting to submit homework often meant being treated to the bamboo stick that lived in the lectern; one could feel all its joints as they landed on one's reddened palms. Tong was familiar with this discipline, which was why it was both surreal and effective when he had raised the instrument menacingly at the class.

Weeks passed; our class lived in silence under Tong's rule. We were winning awards for being the quietest class during the siesta period, and all our instructors congratulated Mrs. Yang on her decision to put the least promising candidate in the position of Silence Manager, with brilliant results. People occasionally made reference to the First Emperor of the Ching Dynasty, a notorious tyrant, or emperors Cho and Yang of the San and Xua Dynasties.

One wet afternoon, as the monsoon rain poured outside the window, muddying the campus and overflowing uncovered sewers, a notice came from the discipline office that our military class was canceled because our teacher, army officer Peng, was sick. This automatically made the next hour a study period, and Tong marched to the front of the classroom, imitating Peng's walk. Most of us had learned not to pay any attention to him by now, our heads inclined towards the books and notebooks on our desks. The room was silent except for pencils and pens scratching paper, no student even pushing a chair back or leaving temporarily to throw away scrap paper, for fear of disturbing the uniform silence we had by now become accustomed to.

Then, in the back of the classroom, a pen dropped. Then a notebook. Then a thick textbook slid noisily to the floor. The owner of the book swore and one of his neighbors chuckled. The boy whose things fell wasn't happy about being mocked, and he reached over and pulled the laugher's notebook to the floor, slurring, "O-ops."

The two began pushing each other and most of the class turned around to watch them. Tong glared at the boys, cleared his throat, and finally each of them picked up his books and sat down sullenly, muttering curses involving one another's mothers and brothers.

But a disturbance had occurred and somehow this triggered the entire class to begin talking. Tong's friends laughed loudly. A group of girls who sat near the window side of the classroom giggled, exchanging notes. Someone coughed, followed by the loud clang of a metal pencil case falling to the cement floor, spilling its contents. The volume of the sea of voices rose. Tong tried to talk over the noise, but nobody paid attention to him. He lifted the bamboo stick out of the lectern, held it in his hand, and stared at the rest of the class. One of Tong's friends pulled a basketball out from under his desk, and four boys were now mock dribbling it between their seats, laughing and making a racket.

Wan Jun, the step-sister of some gangsters and also a good friend of Tong's, stood to straighten her dress, smooth her hair, and smile at the class, turning slow circles and swaying her hips as if she were in a beauty pageant. Most of the class was laughing now, whistling, clapping, hooting. Wan Jun bowed in four directions, saying *thank you* to her audience and sat down, making a display of spreading her skirt around her chair like a princess. Tong's face turned green. But nobody seemed to notice; nobody cared about the Silence Manager anymore. We could clearly see that he wasn't doing anything about the noise, and that we could talk if we wanted to. After all, who the hell was he? Gangster boy with a pretty face.

Tong walked out the front door and we thought he had left to fetch a discipline officer, but then *bang,* one of the glass windows of the classroom shattered, Tong's fist and arm coming through it, and the class was instantly mute. He stormed back in with his injured arm dripping blood and said in a forced steady voice to Wan Jun, "Get a taxi and bring me to the hospital."

They left. We were stunned.

The Cleanliness Manager got up and slowly began wiping the blood beside the lectern with an old mop. The rest of the class sat there, murmuring and whispering while she took a broom and dustpan from the closet to sweep up the glass.

"It's Mrs. Yang's fault. She made a bad decision."

"But we made him angry. Though nobody knew that he'd be *that* angry; he was like a crazy man! Did you see all that blood?"

"I saw something like this in a Hong Kong fight movie, *Flying Dragons in the Alley*. I bet Tong was imitating the star. The guy who broke a glass in the movie was much bigger and taller than him, though."

"I feel so bad. Before Tong hurt himself someone could have done something, but now he went and smashed his fist."

"What if he dies from bleeding in the taxi?"

"Shush. How can you say such a thing? Don't curse him."

"Do you think he'll be able to write again? He writes with his left hand, you know."

"I think he smashed his right arm, actually."

"Well, I'm pretty sure it was the left."

Mrs. Yang refrained from talking about the incident when we saw her again. Tong did not resign from Silence Manager, though the teacher invited him to. Now he stands in front of the classroom with his white cast covered with classmates', friends', and gangsters' names and doodles. There is now a certain hardness and bitterness in his beautiful face with the woman's lashes. The sling holding up his injured left arm gives him power over us; the fact that he can't write for at least a month, or use chopsticks, or play basketball properly, makes us feel guilty—but we don't know for how long. There are two more years of junior high, enough time for his arm to heal, get smashed, then heal again—many more times. ༄

After the Stroke

Margot Zucker Mindich

A large red poppy
crowds my father's brain
jams the place
where words are formed.
Mute, he looks at me,
he is still
except for his hands
which flutter upward
from his chair
like two white butterflies.

&

What Were the White Things?

Amy Hempel

These pieces of crockery are a repertory company, playing roles in each dream. No, that's not the way it started. He said the pieces of crockery play roles in each *painting*. The artist clicked through slides of still lifes he had painted over thirty years. Someone in the small, attentive audience said, "Isn't that the cup in the painting from years ago?" Yes, it was, the artist said, and the pitcher and mixing bowl and goblet, too. Who was the nude woman leaning against the table on which the crockery was displayed? The artist didn't say, and no one in the small, attentive audience asked.

I was content to look at objects that had held the attention of a gifted man for so many years. I arrived at the lecture on my way to someplace else, an appointment with a doctor that my doctor had arranged. Two days before, she was telling me his name and address and I have to say, I stopped listening, even though—or because—it was important. So instead of going to the radiologist's office, I walked into a nondenominational church where the artist's presentation was advertised on a plaque outside: "Finding the Mystery in Clarity." Was this not the opposite of what most people sought? I thought, I will learn something!

The crockery was white, not glazed, and painted realistically. The pieces threw different lengths of shadows depending on the angle of the light in each painting. Sometimes the pieces were lined up touching one another, and other times there were gaps. Were these gaps part of the mystery the artist had in mind? Did he mean for us to be literal, to think: absence? He said the mind wants to make sense of a thing, the mind wants to know what something stands for. Okay, the artist said, here is what I painted that September. On the screen, we saw a familiar tabletop—objects familiar from years of his still lifes—but the two tallest pieces of crockery, the pitcher and the vase, were missing; nothing stood in their places.

Ahhhh, the small, attentive audience said.

Then someone asked the artist, What were the white things? He meant what were the white things in the other paintings. What did they represent? And the artist said that was not a question he would answer.

My mother, near the end of her life, announced that she was giving everything away. She was enraged. She told me to put a sticker on anything I wanted to keep, but every time I did, she said she had promised the thing to someone else. The house was all the houses I had grown up in. The things I wanted to keep were all white. But what *were* the white things?

After the lecture, I tried to remember what I had wanted to keep. But all I could say was that the things I wanted to keep were white.

After the lecture, a call to my doctor's receptionist, and I had the address of the specialist. I wasn't so late that he wouldn't see me.

When the films were developed, an assistant brought them into the examination room. The doctor placed them up against lights and pointed out the distinct spots he said my doctor had suspected he would find. I told him I would have thought the spots would be dark. I said, Is this not what most people would expect?

The doctor told me the meaning of what we looked at on the film. He asked me if I understood what he said. I said yes. I said yes, and that I wanted to ask one question: What were the white things?

The doctor said he would explain it to me again, and proceeded to tell me a second time. He asked me if this time I understood what he had told me. Yes, I said. I said, Yes, but what were the white things? ❧

Being Nursed by Walt Whitman

Jennifer Santos Madriaga

My students are all dying.
They come in, one at a time.
I guide them, giving them springboards,
demonstrating to them the power of repetition
by reading Walt Whitman aloud—
I celebrate myself, and sing myself

Each week, it is a different woman.
They are missing parts of themselves—
a leg, both breasts, an ovary, a uterus.
Yet they always smile, if a little wearily,
talking about the book they would like to write
because they have something to say,
even if they are not sure what should be said.

My students are dying,
but they like Walt Whitman.
They like the part about the child asking
What is the grass?
I foolishly forget that the grass
is the *beautiful uncut hair of graves*
until I hear Diana read it aloud.
I thought this poem celebrated life;
I had forgotten the ruminations
on death. We alternate reading
stanzas—

What do you think has become of the young and old men?
And what do you think has become of the women and children?

Every week, a different woman reads.
I hear that some have more bad days than good.
I don't know if I will see them again.

What is the grass?

It may be if I had known them I would have loved them.

My father asks me what it's like to teach
writing to dying people. "Are you afraid?"
"Dad, we're *all* going to die," I say.
"Yes," he says, "you're right."
There's a brief silence as static crackles
on the long distance telephone line.
"You're right, absolutely right."

There are times no one shows.
I wait the full hour out in case someone
has problems managing portable
oxygen or wielding crutches.
Sometimes I almost leave, and then
Diana will come in, breathless, apologetic,
embarrassed by her lateness.
"I always wait," I say. "It's okay."

I celebrate myself, and sing myself,
And what I assume you shall assume,
For every atom belonging to me as good belongs to you.

And then we come to the question
What is the grass?

I know that it is not only her wondering:
What do you think has become of the young and old men?
And what do you think has become of the women and children?

We are afraid and not afraid.

All goes onward and outward, nothing collapses,
And to die is different from what anyone supposed, and luckier.

Not one woman has said she is lucky.
Is it lucky to have received the opportunity of living,
even as we draw closer to an ending no one wants?

What is the grass?

It may be if I had known them I would have loved them.

Each woman reads, voices with
different timbres, distinct intonations.
Time and time again there is the grass,
the wide expanse, the large horizon.
There is the grass, and it's summer,
and the world blooms outside the window,
it blooms when we are here,
it blooms when we are gone.

They are alive and well somewhere.
The smallest sprout shows there is really no death.

What is the grass?
A field that stretches—
A hand, a touch, a smile—
Voices, breathing, pausing.
A crutch, a leg, a smile.

᛫ॐ᛫

Morning at Fifty

Alan L. Steinberg

"Let us go and make our visit."
T.S. Eliot

The drive to the nursing home always occurred in three stages. The first, which took Ebstein past the confines of the city, Ebstein experienced in a purely mechanical way—as if he were a taxi driver. He focused on the workings of the car, how the engine sounded, how responsive were the brakes. He scanned the instrument panel, noting the oil pressure, the engine revolutions, the gas level. He felt like a race-car driver on the morning of a race, or a jet pilot just before takeoff. He was all business, all concentration.

The second stage, which took him from the outskirts of the city to the nursing home, was the worst, the one he dreaded the most. His absorption in the mechanical details of the automobile gave out, and he was left face to face with the horror of what lay ahead: the building of the zombies, where the dead lay waiting to die again. His heart would race, and he would feel weak and hollow. Sometimes, he would break out in a cold, seeping, sweat that chilled both his body and his soul. He had to fight the impulse to suddenly turn the car around—or into the oncoming lane of traffic.

The last stage, as he neared the actual building, was one of preparation. The panic subsided as quickly as it had arisen. He took a deep breath, composed himself. He checked to see that he had the chocolate, or the flowers, or the miscellaneous items that his father needed, or that Ebstein thought his father needed. He took his last sweet breaths of untainted air, aimed the car at the parking lot, and began the ordeal.

As Ebstein climbed the cracked stone steps of the nursing home, which the rain had darkened and dampened but had not scoured clean, he armed himself with kindness, wore his smile like a surgical mask to protect him from the contamination of decay. He knew many of the residents by name—like Achilles in Hades. He could decipher their moans, translate their shrieks into desires. Willy, the curved man, who had been a backhoe operator for fifty years, sitting hunched over the levers in his cell-like cab till his back had rounded into the shape of a cup hook, and who walked now with his eyes closed, crying out in perfect iambs, "I want my pipe and tobacco," till an aide fetched him and brought him blind and shuffling to the smoking room. Agnes, the scowler, who would say with perfect reasonableness, "I've got to get out of here. Help me get out of here," but who was too frightened to take a step beyond the front door. And the lady-with-no-legs who always smiled and who patted his father's hand, saying, "Look who's here. Look who's come to visit," though she herself hadn't had visitors for years.

His father was where he almost always was—in his room, in his stuffed chair, looking out the window at the walled-in garden beyond. Whatever he saw there through his cataract-dimmed eyes seemed to make no impression on him. He never spoke of it, not even when Ebstein called his attention to some detail—a squirrel or a bird, or even someone walking. What he saw when he looked, or if he saw anything, Ebstein would never know. It would be just one more blank space in his father's life, another chasm that lay between them that he would never cross.

Ebstein's father shared his room with Sam. Sam was a big man, with thick arms and a thick neck, but soft now and clumsy, muscle turning into fat unevenly; it took two or three of the young female aides to maneuver him around. Even though he could see, he almost always kept his eyes shut so that Ebstein thought of him as a blind man. Watching the aides struggling to lift him and guide him to the bathroom or the dining room always made Ebstein think of Samson at Gaza. Mostly Sam was silent, but periodically he would start shouting, saying things over and over, stuttering almost, the words never quite complete, never quite making sense.

Today Sam was in his chair, tied to it, really. The aides had devised a system whereby they wrapped the long belt of his robe around the back of the chair and fastened it, so that he wouldn't suddenly get up and crash into something. Rubbing his big, dry hands together over and over, Sam sat quietly for the moment, for which Ebstein was grateful.

Ebstein took a deep breath and walked over to his father, touching him on the shoulder. His father seemed to him so small now, so frail and shrunken that he wondered how he could ever have seemed so vast, so threatening. Is this what life does to you, Ebstein wondered, take you and drain you and leave you like the dry stiff husks of flies dangling in spider webs? Or was it only that his father's anger and disappointments had taken a toll inside, hollowed him out, as it were? Each time he touched his father, Ebstein had that momentary dread that his father would just shrivel into nothingness, disintegrate into a small heap of dust at his feet. He could almost picture himself standing there while the aides in their white uniforms swept up the dust, saying, "What have you done to your father?"

But the dread passed, and his father merely looked up at Ebstein with those watery-dull eyes that neither rejoiced nor condemned, recognized nor greeted.

Ebstein had seen eyes like those, hundreds, thousands. They were the eyes of those who had given up hope or had hope wrung from them—those standing in lines waiting for something, anything, to happen; those standing behind the bars or fences looking out at the world they could never reach; those left barely alive after the war or the revolution or the hurricane had moved on. They were the eyes of those who had passed beyond hope or hate; who had passed beyond even resignation to something more primitive, less human. They reminded Ebstein of the bulbous-eyed look of dead fish. Every time Ebstein saw that look, he said a silent prayer inside his head—to the Universe at large, to whatever forces created it or guided it: "Please let me die before I look like that."

Ebstein could not understand why his father did not die, did not will himself out of this terrible existence. Sometimes, Ebstein felt a tremendous anger well up within him. For a moment, he felt like screaming at his father, shaking him violently the way his father used to shake him and his sister. "Don't you know it's time?" he felt like shouting. "Don't you have any sense of shame?"

But that rage, too, passed and was replaced by a quiet sadness—a general sympathy for all that was living and dying, himself included.

"Good morning," Ebstein said, the old ritual beginning.

"Good morning," Ebstein's father answered, sitting there patiently, head upturned slightly, fish-eyes full of translucent light.

Ebstein never knew how things would go. Sometimes, it seemed his father knew exactly who he was. "You're my son," he would answer when Ebstein asked. Sometimes, he would turn to an aide who chanced by. "That's my son," he would say. Sometimes he seemed pleased to see Ebstein, as if Ebstein's presence, his flesh and blood, his forced smile, his words, all were a kind of comfort to him, like a warm blanket on a cold day. Sometimes, he seemed to Ebstein to be resentful, angry because Ebstein was there, or because Ebstein didn't come often enough, or because he couldn't make his eyes clear again, or his hair grow or his strength come back, or because he wasn't going to stay long enough. And there were times, it seemed to Ebstein, that his father didn't even know he was there, or care; that Ebstein was just one more shape floating indistinctly past him, one more vague and threatening shape before his great bulging fish-eyes. Ebstein himself felt insubstantial then, as if he were without weight and substance, as if he himself and his father and all his life were but a mist the next good wind could blow away. On those days, Ebstein could barely stay half an hour, looking every minute at his watch, hearing his own words echoing hollowly off the white walls, aching to get outside before he evaporated into nothingness, desperate to get into the car and hear the comforting roar of its engine and glide down the highway, the wind warm or cold against his face, stinging him or cooling him with the comforting molecules of existence.

"Do you know who I am?" Ebstein asked hopefully.

A smile, barely, formed on his father's dry lips, but the cataracts clouded the eyes so that no human expression registered there, just round, dull pupils floating in a gray primordial sea.

"You're my son."

"Do you know what day it is?"

"The day my son comes," Ebstein's father intoned, but already the voice was beginning to disengage, Ebstein sensed, to break off again, as it were, from the reality of the moment.

"I did. I did. I did. What a goddamn time. What a goddamn time…"

It was Sam, his voice booming, as if he were talking to someone across the room, across the street, even. He was rocking back and forth in his chair, still rubbing his hands together. His eyes were clamped shut.

"It's my birthday," Ebstein said, bending closer to his father, trying to be heard above Sam shouting, "You know that. You know that. You know that."

"Your birthday?" Ebstein's father asked, as if he could really understand.

"What a goddamn time. What a goddamn time."

"Do you know which one?" Ebstein implored. "Do you know how old I am? Guess."

"It's my son's birthday," Ebstein's father said, but whether it was a question or a statement or just mindless repetition, Ebstein could not say.

"Everybody said so. Said so. Said so."

"I'm fifty today," Ebstein said. "Fifty. Half a century." Ebstein hoped against hope that putting it that way would break through the fog he could almost feel thickening and settling between them.

"Fifty?"

"The people don't know. The people don't know," Sam shouted, rubbing his hands more vigorously. "The people don't know a goddamn thing."

"Yes. Can you remember when I was born? Fifty years ago. Can you remember that long?"

"Yes," Ebstein's father said.

"I did. I did. I did that time."

Ebstein looked at his father, tried to put the word together with his father's expression, the gray fish-eyes. "You do?"

"No matter how it happens. No matter how it happens. No matter how," Sam bellowed, his hand rubbing reaching a furious pace.

"Can you tell me?" Ebstein said, afraid to hope; afraid not to. "Can you tell me what you remember?"

"Not a goddamn thing. Not a goddamn thing."

Ebstein waited, looking at his father sitting there, small and frail, also waiting. Patiently waiting. But waiting for what? For the aide to come? For night? For tomorrow? For death? Ebstein bent even closer, took his father's chin in his hand, lifted his father's face to his.

"Do you know what I'm asking? Can you understand me?"

Ebstein's father said nothing.

"I did. I did. I did," Sam said, his shouting beginning to subside.

Ebstein sighed, removed his hand from his father's face. The road home is never easy, he thought. There are no shortcuts. History is never complete, not even your own.

"Yes," Ebstein's father said into the silence, his voice steady, firm.

Ebstein bent close again, hope flickering. "Yes, what? You remember? You understand? Tell me what." There was urgency in Ebstein's voice. But already he felt the moment slipping away, the room darkening. Ebstein's father, like Sam, had closed his eyes.

"Do you know what day it is?" Ebstein asked softly.

Silence.

"I had a time. I had a time. I had a time," Sam said, his voice soft now, almost a whisper. And then he, too, was quiet.

Ebstein took out the chocolate that had nearly melted in his pocket, broke off a small piece and put the rest of it in his father's hand, gently folding his stiff fingers around the sticky wrapper. Then he walked over to Sam and touched him on the shoulder.

"Here's a piece of chocolate for you," Ebstein said.

Silence. Silence. Silence. ೞ

First Steps

Floyd Skloot

After fifteen years
my first steps
without a cane
are quick and stiff.

I am dizzy with freedom
and not the tottering child
or Frankenstein I'd imagined.

Wild in the torso but a little prim
in the hips, I still have a long way to go
before calling this a walk and I'm not sure
if I dare look away from the ground before me
because wind rippling through leaves makes me dizzy
and the last thing I need at this point is to fall on my face.

I didn't plan for this. If there's one thing my damaged brain
has learned by now, it's to make no plans, have no expectations
and accept whatever the new day brings. Today I forgot to take my
cane with me when I left home for a walk. As soon as the door closed
I realized I was empty-handed and stopped dead. I had to smile. Freud!
Forgetting Intentions and Bungled Actions! Maybe I did plan this but did
not know. Which would be consistent not only with Freudian interpretation
but with brain damage as well. All right, I would follow through and see where
this led me because another thing I've learned since getting sick is that the body
knows things that the mind does not. It was time to look up. To gaze at the road
ahead.

≈

Midnight in the Alzheimer's Suite

Floyd Skloot

Lost in the midnight stillness, my mother
rises to dress and begin another
chilly day. She crosses the moonlit floor.
There is too much silence beyond the door,
and a lack of good cheer, so she breaks
into song. But the coiling lyric snakes
back on itself and tangles in her throat.
She stops long enough to see a cloud float
along the hall, but somehow the cloud speaks
in the voice of the night nurse. Someone peeks
from a doorway. Now someone starts to moan,
someone else coughs and my mother's stray song
returns for a moment: *oh you belong
to me!* If the audience would quiet
down, she would remember. Opening night,
that's what this must be, and the curtain parts,
and the spotlight is on, the music starts,
but there is too much movement, too much noise,
yet she cannot stop, must maintain her poise,
smile and keep on singing. Then it must be
over because the night nurse is there, she
embraces my mother and leads her back
offstage, whispering, bringing down the dark
again. Tired, but pleased with her last set,
my mother lies down for a well-earned rest.

℘

Opposite Ends of the World

Steven Schwartz

Everett whistled for his dogs. They jumped up immediately and waited by the door. Earlier that morning, two animal control officers—were they called officers?—had come by to report a complaint about Cissy and Alberta. A neighbor had filed the complaint; that's all the animal control people would divulge. If he wanted to know more, specifically the names of his dogs' accusers, he needed to send a formal request to the county.

He'd been handed a sheet of paper with friendly bright orange lettering: TIPS FOR CONTROLLING YOUR PETS. Don't leave them alone all day. Don't leave them in the hot sun or freezing cold. DO give them plenty of attention, water, food and exercise. DO remember the three R's: Routine, Reassure, Reward.

At the front door, he put Alberta on the double leash first, then Cissy, who acted the older sister, less frivolous, more cautious, two chocolate labs from the same litter. Last week, Alberta had run into a fire hydrant and knocked herself out. She stood up after a moment and gave her lean brown body a hearty shake, as if to say, *Whew, that was different.*

He identified with her clumsiness: his own stiff-legged walk, his MS. He couldn't ride a bicycle anymore. He'd loved riding, and it was the thing he missed most, but he couldn't even lift his leg over the bar to get on and off now. Swallowing his pride, he'd gotten a girl's bike but he needed toe holds to keep his feet on the pedals. A few days before, he'd ridden around the park; he kept falling and getting up, strapping his feet in, falling and trying again, until his ankles and feet were raw and lacerated. Lauren winced when she saw him (he'd stupidly—or intentionally—worn sandals too).

Now he walked around the lake, both dogs rasping on their leashes while other owners jogged by high-kneed, with their dogs loping ahead of them on slack leashes. He moved slowly forward in his poky drilled walk, then stopped for a rest in the shade, tying the dogs to the pole of a barbecue grill. Alberta, spotting an irresistible specimen, lunged for one of the park's ducks, until she was yanked back on her chain. The more astute Cissy watched calmly on her haunches as if to scold her sister, *Haven't you learned anything yet?*

"Mr. Stottlemeyer?"

"Kevin, what are you doing here?"

Kevin, fourteen years old, pointed behind him to a bus full of children. It was the junior high where Everett had taught band. "We're going to practice for next Wednesday."

"Next Wednesday?"

"Band Day."

"Oh, yes," said Everett. He'd forgotten. The three junior high schools held their competition here at the park every May. Everett had been in charge of it before he resigned.

"Is Mr. Cramer with you?"

"He's right there," said Kevin, pointing behind him at the teacher who had replaced him a year ago.

Everett put his hand flat on the ground and tried to push himself up. He'd been sitting too long.

"Can I help?" said Kevin. He had grown at least four inches since Everett had last seen him. He played the clarinet, passably.

"I think I can manage," said Everett, but his legs, more numb than usual, wouldn't cooperate. He breathed deeply and tried to picture energy flowing to his extremities. Nothing. "Maybe I'll just sit here a minute more."

"I'll go get Mr. Cramer," said Kevin, before Everett could stop him. He didn't want John Cramer to find him in this position, helpless, unable to get up, maybe unable to stand. That's what he was most afraid of—that he wouldn't be able to remain on his feet once he did stand.

John Cramer, who was forty-seven, ten years older than Everett, came down the hill with a big pleasant smile on his face, his red and white windbreaker—the official school jacket—rustling. He'd heard good things about John, that he motivated the kids, got them to practice, kept their minds focused on the playing. He had them doing songs, Everett had heard, from *Phantom of the Opera*. Not bad.

"Everett, what a wonderful surprise to run into you. How's it going?"

"Fine, John." He extended his hand up for John to shake. "Just out walking the dogs." The dogs hadn't taken their eyes off the lake, the free flying geese. They'd be no help. "I've been hearing good things about the kids," said Everett.

"I'm constantly reminded of the standard I have to live up to. They don't hesitate to begin a sentence with 'When Mr. Stottlemeyer was here...'"

The kids ran up the hill, carrying their instruments. "Would you like to join us for practice today?" John asked.

"Join you?"

"Back to back. You take one side, I'll take the other."

His legs wouldn't have anything to do with the idea. "Maybe some other time. A little tired today," he said.

John nodded sympathetically. Everett thought it must make people more uncomfortable than if he were in a wheelchair, his stiff-legged gait, his shakiness, and most of all the uncertainty of his condition. There wasn't anything predictable about it. One day he might be in remission. Another day it might eventually kill him. "I'd better go before they try to escape," John said, looking up the hill at the kids who were chasing each other in tag, swinging their instruments.

"John, would you mind giving me a hand?"

John didn't hesitate. Everett reached up and grabbed his wrist. He saw the alarmed look on John's face when his wrist was gripped with the tension of a towline.

"Should I pull?"

"As hard as you can," said Everett. He had absolutely no strength in his legs. He felt he would collapse.

He stood, shaky. John kept his grip. The legs—he thought of them as a separate entity: a corporation with its own physical by-laws—had decided to hold. He took a tentative step toward the dogs, the right leg quivering like a plucked guitar string, but it stayed in place. This would work. This would work.

"Are you going to be all right, Everett?"

"I am," said Everett. "Thank you."

Lauren called as he opened the door to let himself and the dogs inside.

"How's it going?" she asked. He could hear her eating lunch at her desk. She was director of personnel for a software developer. The company had grown three-fold in the last two years and her position was stable and lucrative enough to support both of them. They had an affordable mortgage on a modest home in the old section of town, no big expensive wishes. It made sense to both of them that Everett leave teaching. He could devote himself to staying healthy, not tire himself out so much. And frankly he couldn't get around the school, all those steps, marching down the field, the exertion of practices . . . he would have needed a wheelchair, which he couldn't accept. Yet.

They had no children either, though he knew this was not something that Lauren wished. The multiple sclerosis had come unexpectedly into their lives, a burden of such consequence that it had squeezed out hopes for a family: illness was their unwanted, unplanned member, and perhaps if they'd conceived a child before its onset, they would have adapted, but the focus of Everett's nurturing had become his own iffy health. It wasn't fair to Lauren, he knew. But it wouldn't be fair to himself, either. He wanted to help her with the child rearing, yet he worried how much he could realistically do. Worst of all was the possibility of disintegrating right in front of his offspring's eyes. Watch my bladder go, my bowels fail, son. Watch my legs collapse, daughter. He tormented himself with such possibilities, perhaps from fear of humiliation, perhaps from just fear. "I can do the majority of the care-taking," Lauren had told him. "Or we can get help." But at about this time, he fell down a flight of steps, and the fall was bad enough that the subject was just dropped, went underground, along with his best legs.

"I had a little trouble at the park," he said. "I couldn't stand up for a moment."

"Did you take your medication?" Every week he received a package by express mail from Israel, his medication packed in dry ice. He injected himself with the serum and hoped for better things. He didn't even know what was in it, only that his physician had recommended this procedure and the stuff couldn't be gotten in the U.S. He laughed at first—medicine from the Holy Land on dry ice, hugely expensive. Before long he was taking it three times a week, afraid now to stop because of the little relief it appeared to offer.

"I'm going to."

"Don't push yourself," said Lauren.

"I know."

"That means leaving the kitchen alone."

Slowly, Everett had been remodeling the kitchen. It was a project that had turned into a nightmare: 1950's metal cabinets ripped out; the old-style Battleship linoleum, two layers of it thick as tires, needing to be pried up to reach the wood floor beneath; a warren of lead piping dating back eighty years that had to be replaced. He couldn't have picked a worse job.

"Why didn't you start with a bedroom or something simple?" asked his father, a lawyer in Washington. "You always have to tackle the toughest thing." Everett didn't know whether the old man—still going strong in his practice at seventy-four—was talking about the MS or the kitchen. Then again, his father sometimes gave the impression that Everett could beat this thing, if he just put his mind to it. Diseases that lacked known causes and cures baffled the man, a litigator who had lived his life smack in the middle of causal deployments. His mother offered more sympathy but along with it came an entire clipping service devoted to MS developments, subscriptions to newsletters, and—her latest venture—efforts to get him to join a therapy group on the Internet.

He *had* gone to a number of meetings with fellow sufferers, and there was much talk of treatments and sub-treatments (Prozac for depression, Paxil for anxiety), and living with a progressive disease, and he couldn't say that he hadn't benefited from the support and company, but he hadn't gone back, either because he was basically a loner or because, as his group might say, he was still fighting the big stupid fact of his damn luck.

"All right," Everett said to Lauren. He wouldn't put up a fight about the kitchen today. He had the floor ahead of him anyway, pulling up and replacing the rotten boards, then sanding, finishing, and screening—work that was hell on his knees and legs. He'd promised Lauren he'd get someone to do the job, but he couldn't justify the expense when he was home all the time.

"Do something relaxing," Lauren said. "Paint, watch a movie. Remember how we used to watch old black and white movies in the afternoon?"

"We should do that again," Everett said. "Soon." They would close all the curtains, unplug the phone, make popcorn, and curl up on the couch together, watching the movie. Afterward, they'd make love. Film noir excited Lauren in a way Everett couldn't quite figure out. Perhaps it was the toughness of the two dimensional past; she wouldn't have to hire anyone like Robert Mitchum or Sydney Greenstreet for a software job; she wouldn't have to get involved in a grievance suit; she wouldn't have to run a security clearance; she wouldn't have to mediate. These men were just brave or cowardly, noble or despicable, without needing "further evaluation." Something remained dependably heroic or evil about their character and perhaps lust, arousal, yearning, whatever it was that caused Lauren to hurry off her clothes and grab for his belt had to do with that fantasy of a whole and predictable man you could always count on. It was a question he'd given a lot of thought to recently—what exactly constituted his manhood, his completeness, now that he could barely walk? Now that he took medication with Hebrew labeling that affected his sex drive. It required a lot more work than simply sitting together on a couch watching an old black and white movie.

"Don't get discouraged," said Lauren. "It doesn't mean anything that you had trouble in the park."

"Lauren . . ."

"Yes?"

"I . . . I was terrified."

There was silence on Lauren's end. What did he expect her to say?

"I can hear it in your voice."

He swallowed a few times. He'd wanted her to be there; he'd felt so horribly alone.

"I'll be home early tonight," she said. "Will you be okay?"

"Yes," he said, and got off.

One afternoon in 1992, shortly after Everett received the clinical diagnosis of his MS, Lauren informed him, "You'll always be the same person to me, don't you ever forget that." He heard her fierce loyalty seared in the statement, her promise to never leave him, her Lauren-like resolve. They'd been married for two years. They sat in a little park across from the Denver hospital. Lauren started talking to him about changes in diet, alternative therapies, exercise. Their sex life wouldn't, as some people claimed, necessarily take a hit. "And there's only a slight risk of a child inheriting MS," she slipped in.

Obviously she'd done the research and prepared herself for this result, unlike he, who had held out hope that his dizziness and fatigue had to do with anything from anemia to depression. A gentle breeze had blown through a stand of shadowy pine trees above the berm of the Denver park. Unleashed dogs leaped with exquisite arched grace for Frisbees. This may have been the moment when the idea of Cissy and Alberta arose, a vision of their springing muscular canine bodies free from this particular virus or whatever it was that had his own immune system stripping away the insulation of his nervous system, like termites chewing a house from the inside out. "I'm optimistic," Lauren had said, as if she were not only telling but warning him to be as well, her legs smooth and tan from a beach trip to Mexico that they'd taken to get their minds off waiting for the results of all the tests, her hand never leaving his arm, her small mouth pursed with keen determination.

Except for hearing her later that evening crying in the bathroom on the cordless phone talking with her mother, he would have thought, and half believed, everything was going to be all right, and she was neither scared nor disappointed about the rest of their lives. He'd always pictured himself—son of a take-charge father—as the one who would care for Lauren in the event of illness or an unforeseen catastrophe. How humbling and disquieting to see how little say he or anyone really had in the matter.

When he returned from Hardware Hank—he couldn't restrain himself from a trip to rent a floor sander, feeling better after a nap—there was a note on the windshield of the car. It wasn't a note actually, but a thick computer print out. He unfolded the pages and stared at it in amazement:

BARK BARK BARK BARK BARK BARK BARK BARK BARK
BARK BARK BARK BARK BARK BARK BARK BARK BARK
BARK BARK BARK BARK BARK BARK BARK BARK BARK
BARK BARK BARK BARK BARK BARK BARK BARK BARK
BARK BARK BARK BARK BARK BARK BARK BARK BARK
BARK BARK BARK BARK BARK BARK BARK BARK BARK
BARK BARK BARK BARK BARK BARK BARK BARK BARK
BARK BARK BARK BARK BARK BARK BARK BARK BARK
BARK BARK BARK BARK BARK BARK BARK BARK BARK
BARK BARK BARK BARK BARK BARK BARK BARK BARK

BARK BARK BARK BARK BARK BARK BARK BARK BARK
BARK BARK BARK BARK BARK BARK BARK BARK BARK
BARK BARK BARK BARK BARK BARK BARK BARK BARK
BARK BARK BARK BARK BARK BARK BARK BARK BARK

It went on for eight pages. Nothing else. He looked behind him, as though there might be a surveillance camera. What the hell was going on? He thought about his neighbors. A college student who came and went with her boyfriend rented the house to the south of theirs. Everett didn't even know her name. The house on the corner belonged to Mrs. Yemetz, a sweet old lady who wore an apron and greeted him with a big smile of false teeth. She was hard of hearing. On the right side was a young family with two cats, a hamster, a gecko, and a turtle. They were animal lovers and the kids, twin girls, regularly came over to play with the dogs and bake cookies with Lauren, who doted on them. Next to them were the Mikelsons, Curtis and Arlene, childless like themselves. Everett supposed they could be a possibility. Curtis worked out of the house, so he was home all day. But Arlene worked with Lauren at Western Systems and had never mentioned a thing to her about the dogs. And in person they always acted pleasant and friendly enough. They'd even had a few backyard barbecues together, although Everett had quickly run out of things to say to Curtis, who never followed up on a topic or initiated a conversation himself. "What did you and Curtis talk about?" Lauren had asked after one of their get-togethers, because Lauren really did enjoy Arlene's company. Everett had shrugged, unable to say.

He sat down and wrote to the Humane Society requesting the names of Alberta and Cissy's accusers.

The dogs stayed especially docile and quiet the next week, as if suspecting they were the subject of an investigation. They looked up at him with their limpid gray-green eyes, an eerie transparent shade of hazel, unique to the breed: *Who us?* those eyes seemed to ask when Everett would inspect them for signs of misbehavior after he came back from a short errand. They did appear innocent. And Everett received no more notes, no computer printouts. Lauren had told him just to forget about it. If the person didn't have the guts to accuse them to their faces, why care? And if the Humane Society investigated further they'd find out how baseless the charges were.

He spent the whole week redoing the kitchen floor: replacing the occasional damaged board with a matching one he pulled from the closet. With a drum sander, he made the old wood smooth as a pearl, then edged it with the belt sander, screened and applied four coats of polyurethane. When it was done, the original cherry floor shone a rich sunny red—perfectly restored. Lauren was amazed. They stood at the kitchen threshold and admired it.

"I want to eat on this thing as soon as it's ready," she said. He felt inordinately proud, ridiculously happy. It was only a floor! And yet it filled him with the satisfaction of slaying a dragon. Hours later, after they'd gone out to dinner—the solvent fumes hung in the air despite the fans—and after they'd successfully made love, dragon slayer that he was, he stood at the threshold and admired his floor in the dark. He'd renovated it board by board, his fingers cut from prying up the stiff linoleum, his back and legs searing with pain, but good pain, acceptable pain, pain from hard work alone and nothing else. So what if one day he might not be able to walk on it; for now it was solid, gleaming ground.

In the morning, Lauren woke before him, and he heard her showering. He went out to the kitchen and walked across the floor. His legs felt fine. He walked back and forth several times, then sat down in the middle.

"It's beautiful," said Lauren. She stood in the doorway watching him.

"Come sit," he said, and patted a place next to him.

She knelt down—she didn't want to sit all the way in her skirt.

"I'm feeling well," he said.

"Good," said Lauren, but he could see she didn't get what he was saying.

"I'm talking about the MS," he said.

She stared at him. "Really?"

"It feels like this is going to last." He knocked on the kitchen floor, believing it. He'd been thinking about it while he'd worked on the floor, his knees sore, his back aching, the occasional crackling pain down his spine, which he had ignored. If he could lay a new floor, he could have a child. It was that simple and that preposterous.

"You wouldn't joke about this, would you?"

"No," said Everett. "I wouldn't."

Lauren's eyes widened, her face flushed, a pretty rose shade that swept down her neck and startled him. "I'd completely given up any hope," she said. "I mean, about a baby."

She got up and hurried into the bedroom. When she came back she held up her blue diaphragm case. "Should I?" she said.

"Sure," he agreed, unclear exactly what she had in mind.

He followed her out to the garage and watched her throw the egg-blue case in the trash, filled with all the worn boards he'd pulled up from the kitchen floor. The diaphragm case wedged itself there between nailed and splintered wood.

"I'll call you," said Lauren, "as soon as I get to work."

He hadn't seen her so happy, not in a long while.

Dear Mr. Stottlemeyer:

Per your formal request, we are forwarding the names of the complainants as prescribed by section 3098 of the county code. Please be advised that such disclosure does not constitute a waiver of your responsibilities to comply with all recommendations for control of your pets.

This disclosure additionally does not endorse any legal action by the Humane Society on behalf of the complainants.

Complainants:

Arlene and Curtis Mikelson

He couldn't believe it. Arlene! She worked with Lauren. He called Lauren at work.

"You'll never believe this. It's them."

"Them?"

"Curtis and Arlene. They're the dog haters."

"What are you talking about, Everett? Can I call you back? I have someone in the office for an interview."

"Wait! Just don't say anything yet to Arlene. I want to think about how to handle this."

He got off and walked out front. He stared at Curtis's house. Everything was neat and organized. A cedar plaque with their name—The Mikelsons— swung from the spotless porch. Each of the trees in their front yard had a low decorative wire fence, white with half moons along the top. The grass, freshly mowed, not a dandelion in sight, rolled out from the front step like an emerald lake. A hose coiled around its caddy without a kink. Never so much as a leaf on their lawn. No kids ever visited. Their garage was the only one on the block that wasn't filled with junk and actually had room for a car.

He went down the sidewalk. Alberta and Cissy, who had nudged opened the screen door, started to follow. "Stay!" shouted Everett. Why was he yelling at them? They hadn't done anything wrong. "Go back," he said more calmly, and they obeyed, turning to flop down together on the porch, looking at him over their paws.

He knocked on Curtis's door. There was no answer at first, so he rang the bell—two jabbing shrieks. Finally, Curtis came to the door. Tall, awkward, dressed in a long-sleeve flannel shirt even in spring, he seemed to flinch from the sight of Everett, and Everett had a pang of remorse at being there, at how chronically bashful Curtis was around people. Arlene, as happens with couples, was the complete opposite: effusive, warm, spontaneous, always glad to see you. But here was a man who cowered inside, working on complicated circuitry or whatever it was he did. It brought back all the stressful memories of trying to talk with Curtis at the backyard barbecues: Curtis hunched over and listening intently, Everett allowing spaces in the conversation, but Curtis neither responding nor initiating anything of his own. It had unnerved Everett so much the last time, that he'd begun babbling about his MS: when he got it (April 1992), when it went into remission (October 1996) and when it came back (May 2000). The more he talked, the more uncomfortable Curtis became until both men suddenly broke away from one another like a wishbone, flung to opposite sides of the yard, Everett with a spatula in his hands, Curtis simply rubbing his neck, as if he'd gotten whiplash, their wives watching them with curiosity. He hadn't spoken to Curtis since that evening last summer.

"I want to talk with you about my dogs," said Everett. Curtis looked past Everett, as if worried the dogs might actually be on his property. He was yet to open the storm door, forcing Everett to raise his voice. "Why didn't you come to us?" asked Everett. "Why couldn't you simply knock on our door and tell us to our faces that you had a problem?"

Curtis mumbled something.

"What?" said Everett through the glass.

"People are sensitive about these things."

Was this an explanation? Better to secretly report someone than to upset them in person? Or was he afraid of Everett? Is that what he was saying? It gratified him to know someone might be afraid of him in his condition.

"How about if I come in and we talk about it?"

Curtis shook his head. "I don't think we should talk here."

Everett was about to ask, why not? But he decided it wouldn't get him anywhere. Clearly, the man had peculiar ways Everett would never understand. What did Arlene see in him? Did Arlene know he had even complained?

"We can talk at your house," said Curtis. He stepped outside, pulled his door closed and stood with uncertainty next to Everett, waiting for him to move.

They walked in silence to Everett's house. Everett opened the door for Curtis who stepped carefully past Alberta and Cissy, thumping their tails. He followed Everett into the living room.

"Want something to drink?" asked Everett.

"To drink?"

"A beverage." He felt like a flight attendant. What was so difficult to understand? "Water, soda, lemonade?"

"I'll take a birch beer," said Curtis.

Everett stared at him. "We don't have birch beer."

"Water will do then."

Had he made a joke? Birch beer? Curtis hadn't cracked a smile. Everett walked across his new floor. He got Curtis a glass of water. When he came back,

Curtis was peering at the fish tank. "Those goldfish shouldn't be in the same water with the tetras," said Curtis. "They need different pH balances."

"I haven't had any trouble."

Curtis shrugged. He had a thin face and a crown of hair in tight gray curls. He blinked several times after he spoke, as if each sentence took enormous effort and temporarily exhausted him for a few minutes, his supply of communication like one of those 7-Eleven safes that pop out twenty-dollar bills at timed intervals.

"I just wish you would have said something to us first," said Everett. Alberta and Cissy were looking in through the screen door.

"You need to control your dogs."

"But I do control them, Curtis. For God's sake, look at them now, what's the problem?"

"You need to control them," Curtis repeated. He twisted his long body around on the couch, then took a drink of the water Everett had put in front of him on a coaster. "Their barking," he said. "It's so . . ."

"What? Too loud?"

"No."

"What then?"

"Bark bark bark."

Everett remembered the computer printout. "What's that mean?"

"Monotonous. It goes all the time. Bark bark bark."

"When do you hear this 'bark bark bark'?"

"They do it when you leave. As soon as you pull out, they start."

"Really," said Everett. "And you can hear it? Two houses away when they're inside?"

"Yes," said Curtis. He took another sip of his water.

They sat in silence for a long minute. What could he possibly say? "Maybe you're just noticing it now because it's spring and our windows are open."

"Maybe," Curtis mumbled.

"What if I put them down in the basement when I leave?"

"I'll still hear them."

Another minute passed. "What do you suggest I do then?" asked Everett.

"I don't know," said Curtis. "Control your dogs."

"You keep saying that, Curtis, but exactly how do you think that should be accomplished?"

"Give them more to do."

"Pardon?"

"Give them something to do while you're gone. Maybe they could chew on a rawhide bone."

"You think that would stop them?"

Curtis squirmed. After a moment, he said, "What's that noise?"

"What noise?"

"That sound. Hiss."

"Hiss? I don't hear it."

"Listen."

They both went silent. Everett sat motionless, straining to listen.

"You hear it now?" said Curtis. "Hissss."

"No, I'm afraid I don't."

Curtis got down on all fours. He began crawling, his large bony body tracking slowly across the oval rug like a sea creature emerging onto land for the first time. "It's somewhere in here." He was up against the fireplace.

Everett got down next to him. They were both on all fours looking up the flue. "It's the pilot light," said Curtis.

"You hear the *pilot light?*"

"That's it," said Curtis, standing up, satisfied now. He turned and walked toward the door. He started to say something—control your dogs?—then thought better of it, and left.

After Curtis had gone, Everett felt a migraine coming on, his vision distorting. He drew the blinds and lay down on the bed in the dark. He tried to quiet his brain, soften the muscles in his face, picture his clean, unmarred, sunlit floor. He had Imitrex and painkillers, and if that didn't work he could always get a shot of Demerol at the clinic.

Cissy and Alberta scratched at the front door. It was time for their late afternoon walk. He supposed they'd start whimpering soon if they didn't get it. Curtis would hear that too, with his super-sensitive hearing, like one of those big electronic ears that could pick up whispers from across a cornfield. Bark bark bark. Control your dogs.

The phone rang, then rang again, then again. He finally forced himself to answer it.

It was Lauren. She wanted to know how he was. "I have a migraine," he said.

"Oh, Everett, I'm sorry. I shouldn't have called. Go back to bed."

"Okay," he said flatly.

"Can I tell you something?"

He nodded, then said, "Yes," remembering he was on the phone.

"I'm so excited. I can't believe how excited I am."

He was going to tell her about Curtis, but why? What would Curtis have to say about a baby? A screaming child. But maybe that wouldn't bother him. Maybe that was okay because it wasn't monotonous. "I am too," Everett said.

"You still want to?"

"Yes, I do," said Everett.

"I'm coming home to take care of you," said Lauren.

"It's all right," he said. "I just need to lie down and relax."

"You're sure?" asked Lauren. "I really would be glad to."

"It's fine," said Everett. She was the most maternal person he knew who didn't actually have a child. It would be criminal to deprive her of one. "I can't believe it," he added.

"Can't believe what?"

"What we've decided."

She was silent, then said, "So you don't want to?"

"I do." What he couldn't believe, what he couldn't somehow manage to say with his head splitting, because he couldn't raise his voice enough, endure the inflection needed to express such an emotion, was that he and the child—this child he so much wanted too—were at opposite ends of the world, with so much ground to cover in between; it was such a desperate, frightening wish. "I'll see you soon," he said.

"Love you," said Lauren.

He went back into his room and lay there in the dark. It wasn't long before he succumbed to taking two painkillers and closing his eyes for the twenty minutes it took for the pills to work. When he woke up, it was hours later and Lauren was beside him in her nightgown, curled up in sleep. Cissy and Alberta were there on the carpet, fast asleep too, both of them on their sides, their fur shiny. Alberta lifted her head from that position to look over her back at him. He went into the kitchen, across the new floor, stepping stiffly, his legs wobbly. It wasn't any better, after all.

He got some orange juice, then put the empty glass in the sink. He walked outside. The street was empty, the moon obscured by a ragged cloud. The roads were wet and the grass moist. He took off his sandals and stood in the grass, letting the wetness soak between his toes, the blades tickle his bare soles. It had rained hard while he was asleep and everything smelled fresh and fertile, sweet and loamy, a rich beguiling scent, and a taste of early spring and honeyed mornings from the crocuses pushing up. He could see Curtis's house, perfectly kept, quiet, motionless, dark.

Everett began to bark. Once, twice, three times. Bark bark bark. He stood there and barked for almost an hour, strong, potent blasts, until Curtis's light turned on, then off again, and didn't come back on. ✋

And in Spring

Richard Wollman

Time beats with a constant pulse, and pain
in my legs does its best to find new ways
for me to notice, though now there is
a slight lift in the air, the cold the same
as before but with somewhere else to go
as the mud weather comes.

Here by the river hopeful people count
alewives swimming upstream to spawn.
When I try to wake my son to tell him,
I see how his legs have grown lean
disappearing into a blanket like twin fish
as the morning flashes under the current.

&

Memoria

Richard Wollman

> *Robert Wallach, 1961-1968*

I used to see when I looked at you,
two halves, mirrored images—
now I can't fathom where you are
except at night, cold
while I dream of your hands,
their delicately-lined translucent veins
a blue light I can't touch.

I started toward you once.
It was snowing out but colder in.
I was a snow man looking out the window
at my garden's thickening limbs.
I heard myself say, take me
to the place between our yards
where I never stopped throwing
a baseball at a pitch-back
for all the hours you left to me.

You lay in a hospital bed.
I lurked in the schoolyard,
picked fights with boys, taunted them
to feel their tight knuckles pummeling me
until someone would come to end it.

Someone was sent to say you were dead,
but I had already known
because of the quiet outside, the stillness,
the leaves' refusal to harbor the breeze
as the hum of the heat bugs increased.

A lamp burned in your kitchen at night.
I saw your parents and mine, watched them try
to stop themselves from going to sleep,
already beginning to forget
the smallness of your hands,

the timbre of your voice,
shadows you left in the grass.
How quickly you became your objects,
your bicycle, baseball cards I kept
as a hedge against my decaying memory.

*

It's for the living to convey something
of how life is changed, or should have been,
but nothing changes except the need to tell,
to inform the dead of how they leave
their marks on us, give shape to our small grief,
change the arc of a life that might have been.
The evidence of things seems all too indirect.

Or so I think until my own son is born,
his furious heart pumping, his face red,
his lung collapsed like a bag as he struggles
for air. A faint sound leaves his mouth,
chest leaping up, his face my face.
A blizzard of nurses shoves me aside,
takes him to an oxygen tent,
and a voice says, *Do you think he has my hands?*

Lines slip from the pulsing monitors
that count his breaths. *We'll keep him,*
someone says, while I think,
see how he calms himself hour by hour?
I pretend my hand repairs his loss of air,
and he sees me holding him,
and the tubes slide away,
the machines finally quiet as he breathes,
and we leave that place without looking back.

On the eighth day my father holds the baby's legs
near a knife. My son sees himself in the reflection.

You aren't dead, I tell myself as I climb the stairs
to a room where one small boy wakes this night,
calls me, his blue eyes dancing and joy,
to hear me sing, my human voice singing just to him,
while blue geese trumpet in the blue evening.

Knife

Zdravka Evtimova

Autumn was gray and cold.

Few customers visited my shop, perhaps three or four people a day. They watched the animals in the cages, but seldom bought them. The room was narrow and there was no place for me behind the counter, so I, a woman of thirty-four, thin and unremarkable, usually sat on my old moth-eaten chair behind the door. Hours I stared at frogs, lizards, snakes, and insects, which wriggled under thick yellowish plates of glass. Teachers came and purchased frogs for their biology lessons, fishermen dropped in to buy some kind of bait; that was practically all. Soon, I would have to close my shop and I would be sorry about it, for the sleepy, gloomy smell of formalin had always given me peace and an odd feeling of home. I had worked here for five years now.

One day a strange small woman entered my room. Her face looked frightened and gray. She approached me, her arms trembling, unnaturally pale, resembling two dead white fish in the dark. The woman did not look at me, nor did she say anything. Her elbows reeled, searching for support on the wooden counter. It seemed she had not come to buy lizards or snails; perhaps she had simply felt unwell and looked for help at the first open door she happened to notice. I was afraid she would fall, and took her by the hand. She remained silent and rubbed her lips with a handkerchief. It was very quiet and dark in the shop. I was at a loss.

"Have you moles here?" she suddenly asked. Then I saw her eyes. They resembled old, torn cobwebs with a little spider in the center, the pupil.

"Moles?" I muttered. I had to tell her I never had sold moles in the shop and indeed I had never seen one in my life. The woman wanted to hear something else, an affirmation. I knew it by her eyes, by the timid stir of her fingers that reached out to touch me. I felt uneasy staring at her.

"I have no moles," I said.

She turned to go, silent and crushed, her head drooping between her shoulders. Her steps were short and uncertain.

"Wait!" I shouted. "Maybe I have some moles." I don't know why I acted like this.

Her body jerked. I saw pain in her eyes, and I felt bad because I couldn't help her.

"The blood of a mole can cure sick people," she whispered. "You only have to drink three drops of it."

I was scared. I could feel something evil lurking in the dark.

"It eases the pain at least," she went on, her voice thinning into a sob.

"Are you ill?" I asked. The words whizzed by like a shot in the thick moist air and made her body shake. "I'm sorry."

"My son is ill."

Her transparent eyelids hid the faint, desperate gleam of her glance. Her hands lay on the counter, lifeless like firewood. Her narrow shoulders looked even narrower in her frayed gray coat.

"A glass of water will make you feel better," I said.

She remained motionless and when her fingers grabbed the glass, her eyelids were still closed. She turned to go, small and frail, her back hunching, her steps noiseless and impotent in the dark.

I ran after her out of my shop, down the block. I had made up my mind.

"I'll give you blood of a mole!" I shouted.

The woman stopped, followed me back into the shop, and covered her face with her hands. It was unbearable to look at her. I felt empty. The eyes of the lizards sparkled like pieces of broken glass. I didn't have any mole's blood. I didn't have any moles. But I went into the tiny back room of the store and closed the door, so she could not see me. I imagined the woman in the front room of the shop, sobbing. Perhaps she was still holding her face with her hands. Then I locked the door of the back room and found a knife on a shelf. I cut my left wrist. The wound bled and slowly oozed into a little glass bottle. After ten drops had covered the bottom, I opened the door to where the woman was waiting for me.

"Here it is," I said. "Here's the blood of a mole."

She didn't reply; she just stared at my left wrist. The wound still bled slightly, so I thrust my arm under my apron. The woman glanced at me and kept silent. She did not reach for the glass bottle. Instead she turned and hurried toward the door. I overtook her and forced the bottle into her hands.

"It's blood of a mole!"

She fingered the transparent bottle. The blood inside sparkled like dying fire. Then she took some money out of her pocket.

"No. No," I said.

Her head hung low. She threw the money on the counter and did not say a word. I wanted to accompany her to the corner. I even poured another glass of water, but she would not wait. The shop was empty again and the eyes of the lizards still glittered like wet pieces of broken glass.

Cold, uneventful days slipped by. The autumn leaves whirled hopelessly in the wind, giving the air a brown appearance. The early winter blizzards hurled snowflakes against the windows and sang in my veins. I could not forget that woman I'd lied to. For days, no one entered my shop and in the quiet dusk I tried to imagine what her son looked like. The ground was frozen, the streets were deserted and the winter tied its icy knot around houses, souls, and rocks.

One morning, three weeks later, the door of my shop opened abruptly. The same small gray woman entered and before I had time to greet her, she rushed and embraced me. Her shoulders were weightless and frail, and tears were streaking her delicately wrinkled cheeks. Her whole body shook and I thought she would collapse, so I caught her trembling arms. Then the woman grabbed my left hand and lifted it up to her eyes. The scar of the wound had vanished but she found the place. Her lips kissed my wrist, her tears made my skin warm. Suddenly it felt cozy and quiet in the shop.

"He walks!" The woman sobbed, hiding a tearful smile behind her palms. "He walks!"

She wanted to give me money; her big black bag was full of different things that she had brought for me. I could feel the woman had braced herself, her fingers had become tough and stubborn. I accompanied her down the block to the corner but she only stayed there beside the street-lamp, looking at me, small and smiling in the cold.

It was so cozy in my dark shop now and the old, imperceptible smell of formalin made me dizzy with happiness. My lizards were so beautiful that I loved them as if they were my children.

In the afternoon of the same day, a strange man entered the shop room. He was tall, scraggly, and looked frightened.

"Have you...the blood of a mole?" he asked, his eyes piercing through me. I was scared.

"No, I haven't. I have never sold moles here."

"Oh, you have! You have! Three drops... Three drops, no more... My wife will die. You have! Please!"

He squeezed my arm. "Please... three drops!" he cried. "Or she'll die..."

My blood trickled slowly from the wound. The man held a little bottle and the red drops gleamed in it like embers. Then he left and a little bundle of bank-notes rolled on the counter.

On the following morning a great whispering mob of strangers waited for me in front of my door. Their hands clutched little glass bottles.

"Blood of a mole! Blood of a mole!"

They shouted, shrieked, and pushed each other. Everyone had a sick person at home and a knife in his hand. ∞

Medicine Chest

Amanda Auchter

Your face is an old wound.
Yesterday, it stood behind
me while we combed our hair.

Today, nothing, stripped from
the cracked glass. My cage of bone
is hollow, all broken sinews

and valves, stopped dead. I empty
you here—clear the residue
of your skin, wipe the mirror

clean of fingerprints. What is left?
A razor, aftershave, bottle of pills,
tube of toothpaste, your broken watch.

દ્ય

Gesture

Rebecca McClanahan

In the days my father's mother
was dying, the room was busy
with daughters. My father brought flowers,
wrote checks, touched the face
powdered and creamed
after a morning bath.
Their shared breathing filled, emptied
the room. He stared at his hands:
what would be asked?
The Pieta teaches only
how a mother holds a *son*.
As a child too young for his father's
field, he'd followed the dark braid
coiled on his mother's head. The weight
of day loosened it, by evening, pins slid
onto the swept floor. His mother
would sigh, untie her apron
and, still as a child, allow
the undoing: the comb's ragged
teeth, sparks igniting the air,
her son's hands smoothing, smoothing.

 ໙

Pink Ribbon

Gayle Whittier

"The funny thing about cancer," my lunch companion says, "is how it makes you sensitive to language."

"True." We are sitting in the local Applebee's, on high chairs at tables in the bay window. Around us other women excavate salads, dressing on the side. Greens for virtue, vanity, and fear. We women are all a bit afraid of our bodies.

Melissa has already told me about the colleague who asked, "Are you going to lose your hair?" and the book clubbers who shunned her emails, and the many casual acquaintances whose eyes dropped as they inquired, "Which one was it, anyway?"

I keep my eyes on her face.

"Why can't people be more careful what they say, you know?" Melissa asks.

I nod. Beyond the glass, a small snow skitters over the pavement of the parking lot. We are in a new season, the third of four in this first year of our survival. Its spare, sharp shades of black and gray remind me of Breugal without the carousing peasants. "Hunters in the Snow," maybe.

"The waiting-room at Sloan was so tacky!" Melissa complains.

A Sloan-Kettering cancer. Something very serious, exotic, or, perhaps, just a mundane malignancy attacking somebody special. We're both academicians who know how to do research, who can judge the Best, whether it's translations of Homer or imported cheeses or oncologists.

"Sloan-Kettering. I mean, you'd think they'd have comfortable chairs at least."

"Yes, yes," I say. "Who can you trust anymore?"

"Ladies, your salads." The young waitress sets down our two nationalities of lunch, Melissa's Creole chicken on field greens, my Oriental. "Can I get you anything else?...Well, enjoy!" She's wearing a Santa Claus corsage. That's right, it's the time for miracles. I had almost forgotten.

"Everybody brings food to the radiation techs," Melissa says. "I don't know why, exactly, but I did too. I baked cookies and banana bread for them, while we were all living on take-out."

"The raw and the cooked. Well, *food*," I say. "Offerings to the gods, right?" *Bribes*, I am thinking. Gifts and goodies because you are begging them for your life, hoping they will be kind to you and careful, very careful how they burn the breast of that nice woman who brought in the chocolate chips.

We fall silent, spearing baby spinach leaves and royal-colored radicchio and cherry tomatoes and, yes, strips of breast meat.

Melissa and I. Our lunching together might qualify as a minor miracle. Would we even be meeting if not for cancer, and in the same year, like graduates of an exclusive girls' school? We both teach at the local college, but disciplines apart, I in Shakespeare, Melissa in Children's Lit. She's a department favorite. Me? Odd, problematic, on call as needed for assorted blame. She, clever girl, got diagnosed between semesters, convenient for everyone. I, on the other hand, had vanished midterm, stranding students and adding to the workload of my colleagues. Our sisterhood snapped into recent focus under the lens of a microscope, on some democratic, deadly slide. Cancers R Us.

"Where you go makes all the difference. You went to Sloan too, didn't you?"

"No. Here."

"Oh. Well, where was I?" Melissa asks herself. "That's it. Radiation. I mean, nobody told me they mark you with indelible ink. It's to target the, you know, place. It was so...so...They leave you all alone under this huge machine..."

"Ladies?" The young waitress touches base. "Everything okay?" She rotates away again.

"It's pointed right at your breast," Melissa says. "I just kept imaging, you know? I do guided imaging, thinking of rads, I mean *rays*, as warm beads of light vacuuming up the...Where did you go for yours?"

"Actually, I didn't..." I didn't need to is what I don't say.

"The worst part was the waiting room! Looking at all those people, wondering... But Cheryl, she said it's insurance. Insurance," Melissa repeats.

"Cheryl's wonderful."

We agree on that. We both have been shepherded, mothered, really, through the "treatments" for our gendered cancers—her breast, my uterus—by the same kind nursing professor. Cheryl escorted me, tranquillized, robotic, for the MRI to search out death's little cellular way-stations "beyond the primary." The night before surgery, she coached me through post-op. "It will hurt, but you have to cough," she said. She reminded me to drink ginger ale, lots and lots of ginger ale. But not water, which could cause nausea. I watched her, amazed. Why, she thought I was going to live! She prescribed Cream of Wheat for anemia because I had given so much blood to be transfused back to me, self to self. "Autologous donation," they called it. One less stranger with an intimate share of me. "Don't pull yourself up the first time," she warned. "Make a splint, hold it over your wound, and roll." "Wound," she had said, as they all did, as if I had been in an honorable war. She warned me to dangle my legs over the side of the bed before I tried to stand. Because anyone might fall off the edge of such an experience.

"Are you listening?" Melissa asks. "Are you okay?"

"I'm fine. By the way, how's…" I search for her son's name. "…Tommy? It must be hard on him. A teenager and all."

"Oh, well, he's got his own life. But I did something I'm really ashamed of," she says, blushing. "This one time I just lost it. I threw a cup at him."

"Therapeutically?" I try not to smile, but Melissa is already smiling.

"I couldn't help it," she says. "I mean, I was waiting for the doctor's report. I was fixing dinner, and he said something smart-ass and…well, I just threw it." Cancer has let her in on a new secret about her placid self. "Of course then *I* had to make it up to him… How did they find yours, anyway?"

I see. We are not going to change this subject. I begin to tell, once more, my story, or, really, its story, the cancer's. That's one of my big discoveries, how quickly trauma tries to organize itself, ferret out Aristotle's beginning, middle, end. Stories comfort us because they have an ending.

I talk. Melissa stops eating. She pins me down with a clinician's eye. That's new, too, that sure, focused gaze that sections off feeling, weighs dark fact. Did she pick it up from the doctors who call you "the TAH in Room 210"? Is it some tricky talent they suture in while you're out cold? No matter. I recite for her the bright shock of belated blood in my underwear, my gynecologist's difficulty in biopsying the lining of a uterus skewed by decades of fibroids, a uterus sprawled like a mandrake root. Not the womb of the Planned Parenthood diagrams, that sweet pink urn with its cuspy handles. "I hate hurting people," my doctor said afterwards, as if it were all over.

But as I tell the cancer's story one more time, I suddenly overhear that "I" have been transformed in the telling. The narrator's voice belongs to someone else, someone not quite me. As if I had gone "right away" to the gynecologist, instead of daydreaming for two more months that the blood was just a quirk, a glitch in an aging body. As if *I* had not had to be drugged dumb just to hear the bad news in my doctor's study. In my telling of me, I am more prudent, obedient, even *grateful* for medicine, as if I never had to recover from its cavalier violence, its suctioning up of identity, its splicing of my life into before and after. "I" have become, in fact, more like Melissa, in whose focused eyes I can see two tiny stalled images of myself.

"I found mine in a vision," Melissa interrupts. "Oh, not in so many words. I was sleeping and this eerie spirit—it was a woman—it embraced me in a dream. She was cold as ice and I just knew. I woke Alan up. I told him, 'I've got cancer.'"

At the next table, one of the other lunchers catches the C-word, stiffens for a moment, then neutralizes it inside so that she can go back to lunch. Some words can do that, startle a group of women as alert as a colony of meercats. "Malignancy," of course—death spelled in the multiple syllables of a dead language—or " biopsy" or "chemotherapy." Even "diagnosed." AIDS made "diagnosed" stand all its own, in mortal certainty of its unspoken object. But these are the clinic's tame, educated words. It is the daily ones that suddenly turn on their hearers. "Found" can betray, especially if neighbored by "too late." In a pinch, "didn't find it…" works too, if the tone is outraged or sorrowful enough. And "spread," of course. "Had it spread?" Single-celled sounds waiting to metastasize in one's consciousness.

"Well, I was just lucky," I finish the story for Melissa. Lucky. The name they give to dogs on doggy death row.

"So, I mean, was there any history of it in your family…?" Melissa asks. She has become my diagnostician. I can forgive her for that. She needs to know. We're not gossiping, after all. We are here to domesticate the fear of death. Serious business for lunch.

"Yes, actually, there was. My mother. She had the same thing." She died of it is what I cannot say.

"Ahh…" Melissa nods, relieved. In classical tragedies, history is always negative, but in cancer, it confers genetic innocence: you got sick through the tricky crapshoot of your DNA, no fault of your own. "So that's how," Melissa says. She raises one hand to her chest as if to pledge to the flag. But a hand always seeks a hurt, and I see now that it was the right one, yes, her right breast, and I look away. Breast, with its double gifts of milk and pleasure. Only a lover's or a baby's mouth belongs where, she confides across the circular table, the surgeon's bruises and the cobalt's scaly burns have warped her flesh. Lesson twenty-two: Don't use your imagination.

"But Alan's been very good about it, very supportive," Melissa hurries on. "I don't know what I would have done without him. Well, for better or for worse, you know…I mean, we're fine, it's brought us closer than ever, really…." She holds up a forkful of lettuce, studies it, puts the fork back down. "Did I mention it was aggressive?" she says.

"Ambitious?" I offer.

"No, *aggressive*. They said it was… Oh, was that a joke? Oh." She takes a sip of her coffee. "The thing is, I'm taking much better care of myself now. Diet. Exercise. Cancer does that. Makes you appreciate life. *You* know."

"Actually, I think of my life as Plan B."

"Plus, I've been reading Deepak Chopra and the Dalai Lama…."

"Still working on your salads, ladies?" The young waitress appears. "No? How about dessert?… No? I'll just bring your check then." We watch the waitress dance her way to the tinsel-trimmed cashier's stand. She's young, her body still has all its animal confidence. I feel Melissa's thoughts and mine connecting. *How cancer-free she looks, that dreamer.* With nothing in front of us now, Melissa leans towards me, sisterly.

"I'm having awful hot flashes," she says. "Sometimes I can't sleep either. I was on estrogen replacement, and now I can't, so I've lost my sense of...well-being?"

"I know." Estrogen, the magic potion. With it, you have the balmy courage to make babies and make love. Without it, consciousness slaps you in the face.

"They said try soy, but I read that's really estrogen too, phytoestrogen, and anyhow it doesn't seem to... And," her voice sinks lower, "I can't concentrate. I mean, just sometimes. Not a lot. I just forget things...."

"Amnesia isn't always so bad. And it'll pass. Really it will. I can't take estrogen either, you know."

"You won't believe what Dr. Drew said. I'd just gotten back from New York...and he walked into the examining room and said, 'That estrogen we prescribed didn't give you cancer. It just made it grow faster so we found it sooner.' First thing he said to me!"

"Make it the last. Change doctors."

"I know, I know. Alan thinks so too, but the thing is, Dr. D'd be so upset if I left him. He delivered Tommy, you know.... And every *professional* woman in his practice just begged him for estrogen. That's what he told me. Because otherwise you lose your mental edge. You took it too, didn't you?"

"No, I never did."

"There. You see? You didn't take it and you got cancer anyway, so why should I blame myself?" Melissa tilts her empty cup. "I'd like a little more coffee."

"And now, of course, I'm all out of it."

"Out of...coffee?" Melissa wonders.

"No, edge. Estrogen. It's ten o'clock. Do you know where your ovaries are?"

She lowers her voice. "Oh God, yours wasn't *ovarian*, was it?"

"No."

"Well, then, what...?"

"They wanted to be careful. Nothing's left. I'm a *castrata*."

"A what?"

"*Castrata*. Melissa. I've been castrated. Get it?"

Now there's a C-word you don't find in Children's Lit. There's a word to turn heads. The lunchers at nearby tables snap to attention. They are all trying not to look—what body did that word come from?—but one pair of shocked eyes fixes on me. The eyes are betraying a woman with a chef salad, current coiffure, boiled wool and a Coach bag. She wants to quit staring, but she can't. Her stare starts to melt under its own weight, slowly un-gels from my face, drips lower to my torso, slides to my hands. I see her seeing me, a big woman in a rumpled enigma of a dress. She's trying to figure me out and, yes, it all at once arrives: She is wondering if I am on the road to a sex change, transvestite, headed for transsexual, someone on the other side of the estrogen blanket altogether. And is she really wrong? I can't resist. I wink at her.

"Who's that? Is that somebody we know?" Melissa starts to turn around.

"No, just someone I scared off."

"Scared off? Oh, you're joking. That's what they say about you in the department. How witty." Melissa consults her watch. "What time is...oh, it's getting late. I've got to pick up Tommy at his hockey game. But first I'd better...all that coffee—" She slips off the high stool, slinging her purse over her shoulder, and looks around for the Restroom sign.

"Go ahead," I say. "I'll get the check."

It was in restaurant powder rooms, wallpapered, scented, behind a locked door, alone, in silence, that I first felt space open wide in front of me. Before the doctor's expert diagnosis, this was where I kept seeing plain truth, the bloody smudge on the mucousy tissue, the wet mandala of urine with its telltale rim of brown. The body talking without a single word. Sometimes I just flushed without looking. Other times I pondered the cranberry drop, the viscous scarlet strand, like a Rorschach. Now my stream of urine falls clear and untroubling in the toilet bowl, as innocent as girlhood. But it is innocent only because I am even less than a little girl is, because there is nowhere to bleed from, not because there is nothing to bleed.

"How do you like your new body?" one of the nurses asked. They called the incision "my" wound, always "mine," as if I had been made a present of this scar with its manmade beauty, belly-long and thin and white like a line of careful frost. In the operating room they had found a hernia, too, and repaired that as well. The gynecologist even made something resembling a navel. I read later that no one needs it, really, but that surgical patients feel less human without it. Only Eve, unblessed among women, born of bone, never had one. "How do you like your new body?" God to Adam after His selective surgery. But everyone else forever after bears our common sign of coming from the warm and fleshy chamber I have lost.

Yes, I think, this cancer is "mine." Melissa's is "hers." Different carcinomas for different women. Breast cancer is popular. Melissa has a band of concerned colleagues, a husband, and a "support group." She's already gone on a Cancer Workshop Weekend Retreat in a pretty rural setting. Next spring she will march through the local parks with hundreds of breast cancer survivors carrying pink balloons, wearing pink t-shirts, a show of pink force. Melissa can become an activist for Breast Cancer Awareness; she can urge other women to take advantage of the pink traveling bus that offers on-site mammography in our rural county. The Boob Mobile, I once irreverently called it. If Melissa so desires, she can buy a KitchenAid mixer in mammary pink (profits for research).

She can cleanse herself with boutique soaps the color of plasma, a darker pink ribbon criss-crossed through every rub. She can buy a rhinestone breast cancer logo on eBay, or commission a jeweler to customized one in pink tourmalines. Even her pills are pink, with a little logo-woman stamped into each one.

Women bond over breast cancer. It comes up as chatter at cocktail parties; sisters accompany sisters to be scanned; my cousin's daughter celebrates her fortieth birthday with her first mammogram. Melissa has been drafted into an army of Amazons spreading their calamine-colored banners everywhere. *Breast*, visible and versatile, from bra ads to icons of a Virgin suckling God. She will never be alone again.

And I? A used-up uterus lacks glamour; maybe it even lacks class. Someone has to tell it to leave the room; please, just disappear politely; go turn into medical waste or something, will you? And it is on absence that imagination feeds. In the days leading up to the surgery they also called "mine," daylight flashes showed me to myself paralyzed, a tube arched down my throat, catheter threaded up my urethra, my urine measured in a bag. My eyes would be taped shut, Cheryl told me. The temperature in the operating room would be kept low. She had been graphic. "The table tilts," she said. "They'll have you in all kinds of positions." Only a whore's body is so available.

"A local," I begged the gynecologist. "You do it for Caesareans, right? Why not for hysterectomy?" I still loved consciousness then.

"Do you know where your uterus is? It's too far up. It's almost at your diaphragm. We can only go so high, and if there's any complication…" Because, she said, they never knew what they would find inside the body. "I understand, you're afraid of the loss of control. But a local is out." Her free hand touched my shoulder as she opened the office door. "You just have to trust sometimes. And besides," she said kindly, "you wouldn't really want to *hear* it."

The wound they made on the other side of my oblivion healed all on its own, with just a little help from penicillin. But the mind has to recover from its own ingenuities. I woke up severed from all memory—they had a drug for that too. I woke up washed, dressed in a fresh gown, as astonished as a newborn. "Do you think you can sit up now?" "Can you try to walk?" My body, recalled for repairs, had been returned to me, emptied of this death, but not of all deaths. Sooner or later, one of them would work.

Melissa, returning, waves at me, threading through the clusters of abandoned tables. The lunch crowd has thinned. The waitresses have retired their smiles for this shift. They are cleaning up with long, slow petal-shaped swipes of cloth and arm. They scoop and drag coins and dollar bills across the wet fake wood surfaces, pocketing them. Everybody walks wearily, as if through heavy water. I start to gather up my gloves, car keys, purse.

"Did you leave the tip?—Well, okay, but next time, it's on me." We're suiting up for the December outside. Melissa's arms struggle unequally into her coat sleeves. I know enough not to help her. A pastel loop of ribbon, too small for a bow, too loose for a knot, nods at her collar.

"Come again," someone calls as we walk out into the mineral cold. It's the suspended week between Christmas and New Year's, early darkness, with a chain of headlights stringing the parkway together.

Melissa stops, holds up her hand as if to receive a gift. "Is it going to snow?"

I look skyward too. "No, it's just cloudy."

"I don't mind snow. It's ice I mind. You can't see it and then…" Melissa clicks on her remote and the locks of a nearby car open with a thunk. Its headlights flash too. "It's new. The seats warm up," she says, rolling her eyes. "I didn't even want an SUV, they're so bad for the environment, but Alan, well, you know men. Alan had to have all the bells and whistles. I think it's his reward. You know?"

"I'm just hoping my car starts!"

She faces me, back to the wind. "The funny thing is, I was so *good* about getting checkups every year. Every year. And then, at Sloan-Kettering, they said the cancer had been visible two mammograms before. They showed me on the film. But they said they think they got it all."

"I'm sure they did."

"They said they *thought* so. But I just keep wondering. I mean, I trusted Dr. D., and now, well, you know…I'm playing it by ear, trying to forget between checkups? Live a normal life?"

"Mm. I know." I nod. Both of us now keep calendars with new black anniversaries, new re-birthdays. Both of us count out time in milestones. The funny thing about cancer is that it makes you remember the future.

"They tell you five years," Melissa says, "but I don't know. There's a fifteen-twenty percent chance my kind will come back. I looked it up. They can never say you're 'cured'."

They can, but I do not tell her that. "Sloan-Kettering," I answer. "You're in the best place in the world for…"

She nods because she is supposed to nod. Then, shaking us off, brightening, "We should do this again," Melissa lies.

"Yes, let's," I lie too. "Soon."

We move crabwise against each other, like people bargaining for a doorway, then decide to embrace. We touch each other almost delicately. I feel our bodies beneath the winter coats as if they add up, one mutilated breast, one mutilated belly, to a single rescued woman. Melissa makes a small, striving motion and we both let go. "Take care."

"Take care."

She strides over the snow-streaked blacktop towards Alan's big SUV. I wait in place.

"You're cured," my gynecologist, still in her sea-colored scrubs, rejoiced. "The nodes came back negative. Clear." Afloat on morphine, I thought she had said "pured." What "no's" came back negative? They came back pured. Where had they come back from? She was smiling, so I smiled back. Later, alone in my bed, I wondered if I had simply wished the word audible. But the local oncologist, droning to the end of his long lesson about cell division and the staging of disease, said it too. "You're cured." I had only wanted to know whether he would send me into the room where Melissa had spent her forty days, where you had to bring perishable offerings and offer yourself up, perishable too, for the purifying fire. "I don't think so," my gynecologist had said. "But it *was* high up…It's his call." "I just want to consult with Dr. Kung for a moment. Excuse me…" The oncologist left the room. What would draw a man to gynecological cancer? I wondered.

It was a small, serious room in the Oncology Wing of the hospital. There was no floral picture on the wall, no pile of magazines. You did not come here to pass the time. Below his examining table's bright, cupped stirrups, a retractable basin, just barely visible, waited to be filled.

"Well, we don't recommend radiation," the oncologist decided. "But you need to keep going for pap smears. You can still get vaginal cancer, you know." What do they take out for that? Don't ask, my mind replied.

On the far side of the parking lot, Melissa is climbing into Alan's SUV. I start to call out after her, tell her the word she wants to hear does not make that much difference. I know. I have heard it, twice. Doubt lies in words the way death hides in the body. But knowledge keeps me standing still. In the weeks ahead, the death-fear and the euphoria of survival both will weaken, and we will flail earthward, special not even to ourselves.

The confessions Melissa exposed today will have to be sutured silent, so that she can live, so that her dignity can repair itself. Both distant and close, we will pass each other in the halls, nervous witnesses trying to unremember. And my unhealed silences? I have another task. I will have to find words for the real story, the story that is mine. All of this is what I cannot tell Melissa. But perhaps she hears me anyway, across our space. Just before she closes the big silver door, she turns one last time, and each of us raises a gloved hand for a moment. An onlooker would find it hard to tell whether we are leaving or arriving in the cold wind of our separate, saved lives. ∽

The Bald and the Beautiful

William Bradley

General Hospital was particularly good today. The trial of Brenda and Jason for Alcazar's murder began, but Brenda did not appear in court. They are both innocent, of course. Framed, most likely, by one of Sonny's enemies. Maybe a foe from the past, back to settle a score. Only one thing's for certain—I'll be tuning in tomorrow.

Ostensibly, these soap operas are just on for background noise, something to fill the silence of the apartment while I write next semester's syllabuses or dust the bookshelves or make notes for my book. But as I do these things, I find my gaze wandering towards the television, where dark, chiseled men have their arms around the waists of slim, gorgeous women and say things like, "You taught me what it means to love." And I find myself ignoring the important, mundane tasks of real life, preferring, instead, a world of mobsters, secret agents, teenage lovers, and evil twins.

And later, as my fiancée and I sit on the couch, watching a documentary or a foreign film, she tells me something she read earlier that day about the roles women played in Middleton's city comedies, and I respond with, "You know, I'm pretty sure that Cameron is Zander's father, but he doesn't realize that he's right there in Port Charles."

Emily is fairly easygoing, and she puts up with a lot of inane comments, but at this she sighs and says, "How can you watch those things?"

"They're da bomb," I answer.

She doesn't say anything. Just tries not to smile. In our graduate student relationship, it is generally understood that she is the serious one, and that I'm the fool she puts up with. She plays the straight man, rolling her eyes and groaning at me. Deep down, though, I think part of the reason we get along so well is that she finds me charming in my goofiness.

So I elaborate. "I like soap operas because the actors get to say things like, 'I will destroy you.'"

"Uh-huh," she says, raising her eyebrows and folding her arms across her chest. "And that appeals why?"

"Well, I mean, it's funny. How many times have you told someone you were going to destroy him?"

"Never."

"Exactly. Me neither. But they say it all the time on soap operas. 'I will destroy you.' It's awesome. I'd love to be able to say dialogue like that. Also, I like it when the guys on the shows are all dark and seductive. They glare out of the tops of their eyes, really intense. Like this." I lower my head slightly and gaze at her with the most smoldering intensity I can muster. Lowering my voice, I say, "I can see the light of a thousand stars in your eyes."

"Ooookay," she says, pushing against my chest and rising from the couch. She walks out of the room, towards the kitchen.

My mother is really the only person I can talk soap operas with. When I was 21 and diagnosed with Hodgkin's disease, I had to move back into my parents' house. My mother and I would spend our afternoons in the living room watching adulterers and blackmailers scheme, while the heroic characters struggled to overcome the obstacles these villains placed in front of them. And the amazing thing was, the good guys almost always did overcome. Sure, the villains might gain a temporary victory or two, and—if an actor decided to leave a show—a heroic character's plane might crash into the Pacific or something.

But the thing about soap operas—and this gets left out when people criticize them—is that virtue is always rewarded, and vice is always punished. If you cheat on your wife, she will eventually find out and leave you for your brother. If you fake your child's DNA test, the real father will eventually piece things together and raise the kid with his new, good-hearted wife. If you try to use your weather controlling device to freeze the entire town of Port Charles—and all of its citizens—in an effort to conquer the world as a power-mad dictator, the device will eventually be turned on you and you will wind up being frozen alive.

I think we can all learn a lot from that.

More important, though, it seems to me that soap operas offer a type of permanence, something you can count on. Actors may change, super-couples may ride off into the sunset, heroic characters may eventually be replaced by younger, hotter bodies that look better shirtless or in a bikini, but you can usually turn on a soap opera—any soap opera—and figure out what's going on pretty quickly. The good guys show their teeth when they smile; the bad guys smirk. The eyes of the villainess will dart about nervously, while the heroine's gaze stays fixed and constant. Storylines may end, but they're guaranteed to reappear a few years later. One character's evil twin will be taken care of, but someone else will have a doppelganger soon enough; the popular couple will face a grave threat to their relationship, but they'll emerge stronger than ever; the character who dies will somehow come back, if he's charismatic enough to have left an impression on the viewers.

As I watched while chemotherapy devoured my cancer—along with the lining of my stomach and my hair follicles—I was struck by the feeling that these shows will go on forever. Many of them—*The Young and the Restless, Days of*

Our Lives, General Hospital—started long before I was born, and will, presumably, continue long after I am gone.

As my condition deteriorated, my mother and I moved from our living room couch to the sterilized furniture of a hospital room (perhaps a dying room) in Ann Arbor. But those beautiful people still appeared on the glowing box, alternately pledging eternal love and planning corporate takeovers. In that hospital room, handsome men made love to beautiful women, while I vomited up mouthfuls of bile, my intestines burned with painful diarrhea, and the lining of my mouth dried and cracked. Things got worse and worse for me, until, until…

Until, at the very last moment, a crack team of medical specialists arrived to administer one last, experimental treatment. Drs. Monica and Alan Quartermaine, Dr. Rick Weber, and Nurse Bobbie Spencer arrived from Port Charles' General Hospital; Dr. John Hudson and Dr. Jamie Frame were flown in from Bay City General; Dr. Ben Davidson came all the way from Llanview, Pennsylvania. "You'll be fine," Bobbie whispered to me as the doctors tried to work a miracle. Fighting back tears, she said, "I won't let you die."

"He's coding!" Ben exclaimed.

"No," Alan shouted as he worked above me. "I won't lose this one. Not him. Not him!"

"Don't you die on me," Monica pleaded. "Don't you die on me."

And suddenly, at the last possible moment, the machinery started beeping rhythmically.

"His cancer!" Jamie exclaimed. "It's going into remission!"

"It's a miracle," John replied, clenching his jaw.

Okay. That's not exactly how it happened, but that's close enough. There wasn't actually a beeping machine, but my doctors did work diligently, and I survived as a result of their efforts. My continued survival—it'll be six years this December—could indeed be considered miraculous, considering how close to cancellation the days of *my* life actually came.

These days, I find soap operas comforting. Cars blow up, pregnancies are faked, lies get told, and people are shot. But none of it is surprising. No one has ever watched a soap opera and said, "My God! I can't believe that happened!" No one's life has ever been changed by something he or she saw on a daytime drama.

This, I think, is why Emily is so surprised by my fascination with these shows. We both study literature for a living, and we both believe in the transformative power of art. We have long conversations about how the works of Montaigne, Shakespeare, Beethoven, Andy Warhol, Joan Didion, David Lynch, and Tobias Wolff challenge our perceptions, and provide for an enlightened understanding of the world. And we both turn up our noses at movies and television shows that pander or simplify—particularly when they seem to aspire to profundity.

But I still love soap operas. They don't pretend to have any amount of depth, as shows like *E.R.* or *The West Wing* attempt to. The most they can offer is predictability and stability. In a world where wars get launched for dubious reasons, where my livelihood may be threatened by a fickle state legislature's cutbacks in education, and where a 21-year-old is forced to realize that his life can—and will—be snuffed out, probably without much notice, that type of predictability can feel like divine intervention.

I often wish that life were more like a soap opera. It's not that I need more melodrama in my life—I had quite enough six years ago—but their simplified world seems easier to live in. For example, several months ago, when my grandmother died, Emily and I had a conversation about our future, and I had to tell her—as gently as I could—that I will die much sooner than she will; my medical history guarantees it. I will die before her; I will leave her alone. "I want you to be happy," I promised her. "Even when I'm gone."

It was hard for us both, but it was something that had to be said. I didn't feel that we could commit till death do us part until we had discussed what exactly that might mean. I was afraid that she was unaware of the risks, that my own positive attitude and goofy charm might have given her the impression that there was nothing to be scared of, in terms of my cancer and the chances for a relapse or damage from long-term side-effects of treatment.

It turned out I needn't have worried. She tearfully assured me that she understood the risks, the likelihood that she would go on without me someday. That getting married means that, when the relationship ends, rather than divide up the CDs and the books, one person buries the other in the ground. She put her face against my chest and cried, and I reminded her that we are both in perfect health, and would likely live for a long, long time.

And I wished that life were a soap opera. I wished that, instead of sitting on the couch offering weak reassurances, I could lift her up in my arms, kiss her neck, chin, and lips, and tell her, with certainty, that things would always be good.

"There's never anything for you to worry about, ever again. When I'm thoughtless or cruel, it's not me; it's my evil twin. If my plane goes down, my car blows up, my cancer comes back, or for some other reason you have to order my headstone, don't despair. It's okay. I will be back, a few years later, in a dramatic, triumphant return. Love never dies, and nor will I."

But since life isn't a soap opera, I just kept my arm around her shoulders and kissed the top of her head until it was time to go to sleep. ༄

Still Life in Number Seven

Bryan Maxwell

A prelude of iodine, a quickening,
a slipping away of friction,
then a slice that seemed to precede
its own motion of graceful opening

into a smoke jellied scene
of avocado and pomegranate.
This was how an abdomen,
quartered off with baby blue sheets,

unfolded beneath an unassuming
blade in my father's double-gloved hands
to reveal, for the first time,
the dirtied secrets of inner slick and color,

a crudeness I knew I could not
ask anyone to explain, a sight I felt sure
belonged back in its drawer. But
perhaps that is why our breathing,

even when it slides along without the help
of the gentle marking hand of a machine,
is so measured. So patiently insistent.
To give us time to sort through

the shifting nervousness
of organs packed neatly away.
To let us see the most ordinary and sterling
face of things: pigment, texture,

light. A table forever set
for two. A wine bottle forlorn
and cold. A bowl of pears
that no one will ever eat.

൳

Erosion

Whitney Scharer

> *One who doesn't reveal his disease cannot expect to be healed.*
> - Ethiopian proverb

For a year you have been planning this trip and nothing will stop you from going. Seven friends, seven days, forty miles through a crescent-shaped canyon in a desert that until now you have seen only in pictures. Your mother laughs when you try on your new backpack and nearly tip over from its weight.

"Why doesn't Sean carry all that stuff?" she asks, pushing your chest with one finger as if you are balanced so precariously that this will be enough to knock you down. With your pack fully loaded, you wonder the same thing. Your boyfriend of three years is eight inches taller than you and twice your weight. Sometimes, when you are lying next to each other, he tells you to make yourself stiff as a log, and he picks you up sideways and bench-presses you, and you grow tired of being his weight before he grows tired of lifting you. But you are determined to carry your share of the gear. No matter that the forty pounds on your back is forty percent of your body weight and only twenty-one percent of his. No matter that your oldest and best friend, Ali, who goes through life with a grace you cannot master, is carrying nothing more than a fleece jacket, the toilet paper, the oatmeal, and her new jelly sandals, about which she cannot seem to stop talking. You picture her leaping effortlessly along the trail behind her boyfriend, Ben, who is weighed down with her gear like a pack ox. Unlike her, you are made strong by sacrifice. You are eighteen, tough and resilient. Your parents are the only ones who know how far this is from true.

"Call me if anything goes wrong," your mother says, and you know what she is talking about, and they are not the idle words all parents say, because something really could go wrong, and she is only allowing you to leave because she doesn't know a way to stop you.

Six months earlier, after failing a routine hearing test at the doctor's, you removed all six of your earrings and sat in radiology under the CT scan machine. When the X-rays came back, you saw for the first time your brain, sliced up in the pictures like an apple. Your doctor used a long stick to point at a murky mass on the side of your X-rayed head. He used words that reminded you of dinosaurs:

cholesteatoma, mastoid, eustachian, and you pictured this shadowy area inside your skull as a pit of prehistoric tar.

You have never done anything like this before. In school you were the quiet one, the one who ditched gym class rather than be picked last for a team, or strolled around the track reading Austen instead of running. Your body, you decided long before you should have, was not built for exertion.

In summer camp they made you play volleyball and you remember the other girls' legs, long and lithe, their arms reaching out at the perfect moment to send the ball sailing, while your own legs always seemed to carry you back and away. Ali would tell you where to stand and shout your name when the ball came your way, but even if you made contact, it careened off the court and into the bushes so often that soon even she stopped trying to help you.

Hiking is different, Ali tells you now. It's all about you—there's no team, no one to compete with but yourself.

As you stash your pack in the back of Sean's car and pull onto the road, you remember the first night you met him, how he stood on the sidewalk after he walked you home, bouncing a footbag back and forth between his feet.

"You're good at that," you said.

He grinned, showing off, throwing his leg back and sending the bag flying above his head to land in front of him, right where it belonged, an electron spinning around the nucleus of his body.

"Now you," he said, and you watched the bag sail towards you, lined yourself up so you couldn't miss, kicked at the air and watched it hit the pavement inches in front of you.

"You'll get better," Sean said, but you never have.

It started as a hole in your eardrum and the skin around the hole kept growing. The skin of the eardrum didn't know how to heal itself, became a tumor that could move to the middle ear and destroy the bones of hearing, or even grow all the way to the brain. The doctor pointed at the X-ray and gave you a tri-fold brochure, indicating that you were supposed to compare it to the picture of your own head. The brochure was designed for small children, had a cartoon drawing of a pink ear with arms and legs and an earlobe-shaped smile. The ear was waving at you. Inside the brochure he showed you a diagram of the inner ear and explained the different parts, told you what parts you have and what parts you don't.

He explained that hearing is the only one of the senses that is purely mechanical, that really it's just physics. Sound waves create pressure changes in the air which move your eardrum back and forth. The eardrum sends this energy to the bones of hearing, which work like levers to intensify the sound and send it on to the main hearing nerve. Without those little bones—hammer, anvil, stirrup—the sound enters the ear but makes it to the brain unamplified.

"Like an electric guitar that's not plugged in," you said.

"Exactly," he replied, smiling at you for the first time that day.

You thought of a diagram you saw in sixth grade science class, each of the body's systems painted on overlapping sheets of vellum. Strip away the layers of your own body in the same way: skin, muscle, veins, and bone. If something as basic as an ear could fail, what's to say the rest won't follow?

You drive for hours, for hundreds of miles. You cross the border between Utah and Colorado at two in the morning, and after several attempts to find a campground in the utter darkness, pull off on a nameless road and park next to a creek. In the morning you unzip the tent to find a No Trespassing sign only three feet away. Everyone else is still asleep. You walk to the river and climb the red rocks at the edge, sitting next to a point where the river's opening narrows between two boulders, sending a cold spray over you in the chilly morning air. Notice how, if you shift your head, first your left ear towards the water, then your right, you can make the roar of the river as loud or as soft as you want. You will use that trick later, in the mornings when the garbage trucks rattle through the alleys, placing your left ear—the good one—against your pillow and creating for yourself a quiet that is both soothing and scary.

There are certain things you are afraid to do. You do not like heights, or moving too quickly on skis or bicycles, or speaking in front of large groups. All of these things elicit similar reactions in you: a feeling of sinking and floating simultaneously, as if the pressure of the particles surrounding you is the only thing keeping you where you are.

Now add the things that the doctor says you should not do, all involving quick pressure changes: you should not fly, or ride in elevators, or drive over steep mountain passes. While the doctor is talking, you take notes on the palm of your hand. What you want to ask, but don't, is what will happen if you do these things. You picture yourself as a scuba diver emerging from the sea, your body filled with bubbles of air that explode when you reach the surface. You picture your head as a gigantic balloon, filling with air and floating away, filling with air until it's almost bursting, and then with a pop, it's gone.

At first, hiking is easier than you thought it would be: your feet stable, your legs sturdy, the weight of your pack a weight with purpose. You look down at your knees as you move, marveling at the simple machinery of your body. Your knees, with their bony knock-kneed kneecaps, seem suddenly strong, the perfect size and shape to carry you through the desert. The eight of you walk single file, with Sean in front and the rest of you trailing behind at various speeds. You have a general sense of your direction, know you are following a scribble from the topo map that will lead into Fish and Owl Canyon, but so far you can't imagine anything that isn't flat.

You finally arrive at the edge of the canyon and watch as the earth drops away. After miles of flatness, there are suddenly hills descending beneath you, an inverted mountain range. You take off your pack and pick your way carefully to a wedge-shaped rock that has sheared off from the canyon's wall. A small leap and you balance on top of it. The crack between the wall and the rock you stand on is so deep you cannot see the bottom for shadows. Beneath you, miles away from where you are now, your destination is nothing more than absence created by time.

You have not told any of them about your ear. It seems easier to turn your head when they whisper, to move to the right side of them when you are walking, to casually watch their lips when they are talking in a crowded room. A hearing aid will never work for you because it requires an eardrum to capture sound. So the nurse gives you suggestions. She tells you that sitting with your good ear to a wall will bounce the sound toward it; that when you are outside, a floppy hat will achieve the same effect. You try this in the desert, a large cotton sunhat with a string to cinch under your chin.

"I didn't know grandma was coming with us," Ali says, flipping up the brim of your hat and grinning at you. You take it off. Later you grab a flashlight so you can hike back up the canyon for a while and send the hat flying, arcing through the darkening sky like a low-hanging moon before it settles out of sight.

It is not long before you start to question how so many insects manage to survive in such an inhospitable area. There are mosquitoes, there are flies. There are so many flies you hardly want to stop, because the minute you do, they are all over you, seeming particularly drawn to ears and mouths and noses. You don't want to stop but you must, because you are sweating so much that the only thought in your head is of water.

So you stop. You heave off your pack, which no longer seems to hug your spine and has become instead an instrument of torture, the ergonomic straps offering nothing more than various ways to distribute pain. And for a few moments you are free. You are airborne. You jump around on legs that don't feel attached to your torso. But soon the thought of water returns, so you sit on a rock, and you and the flies drink your fill from a bottle which seemed enormously oversized when you began, but which Sean smugly told you would never be big enough, hoisting up his own collapsible gallon jug as proof of his claim. Now yours is practically empty after only a four-hour hike.

"Don't worry," Ben says. "We're almost at the bottom and there will be plenty of water there."

"Oh sure," you say. "Of course." You cap your bottle and put it away, trying not to stare as everyone else keeps drinking. Almost at the bottom turns out to mean three more hours of scrambling from boulder to boulder, and by the time you reach the campground, you've decided that they are going to have to airlift you back out. You are so tired you hardly notice the beauty. Sean and Ben make ramen noodles for dinner, and you remain collapsed next to your bag, trying to look animated enough that they won't notice you're exhausted.

Your surgeon works at the medical center, a sprawling building painted the color of oatmeal. You met with him for the first time a few weeks before the operation, and he shook your hand and laid you down on a padded chair, sliding a plastic instrument into your ear with a camera hooked up to a television monitor. For a few moments you heard nothing besides the plastic probe bumping up against what you assumed were the remains of your eardrum. It sounded so loud you pictured it scraping away at your brain.

"Hmm," he said. "Hmm hmm hmm."

Dizzy, you closed your eyes, and when you opened them again, five medical students stood in a semicircle around you, talking and pointing at the monitor, waiting their turn to peer inside you.

"Get a good look," the surgeon said to them. "It's not every day you have an opportunity like this."

You looked too, as much as you could with your head tipped back, staring up at the milky pink cavern on the television screen, its strange shape gleaming like an oyster's shell and shot through with red veins, like threads meant to keep you stitched together.

You had expected something ragged at the bottom of the canyon, earth ripped apart in a cataclysm, tectonic plates tipped and crumbling. Instead, the landscape is rounded, feminine. The ground exists through a process of selection. The soft shale at the bottom eroded first, leaving the layers of harder sedimentary rock where the river's edge once was, while above, the sandstone was carved into pinnacles and spires by the high desert wind. Nature shaped these rocks by taking others away, and you pitch your tent on what remains.

Your mother woke you up and together you drove through the empty early morning streets. The parking lot at the hospital was crowded, though, and you had to circle up all four levels to the top. When the fourth level appeared to be full, your mother yelled *goddammit* and hit the steering wheel, then dropped her hand in her lap and didn't move it again except to shift. After she parked, you walked together to the surgeon's office, and then to the prep room, where she stood next to you, shifting her weight from one foot to the other.

You would not remember much that happened, but you would remember this: the nurse's cold fingers tapping at a vein in the back of your hand and then the stab of the IV, which she didn't put in correctly, letting it act like a spigot pulsing in time with your heart. Blood seeped out in a puddle on the white cot. You looked for the nurse, but she didn't notice what was happening. You looked at your mom, whose face had turned gray, and you realized for the first time that she was as scared as you were. Finally the nurse came back, *oopsy daisy*, and connected you to the proper tube and blotted up the puddle with a large cloth. By the time you were anesthetized and counting backwards, *ten, nine, eight, seven,* the stain of your blood had faded to the color of dry dirt.

You and your friends are preparing the campsite for nighttime, tying bear bags and weighing down the tents and scrubbing the dishes with sand. When these chores are finished, you sit with Ali on a rock curved like a Barcalounger, stretching out your legs and wiggling your sandaled feet.

"What else can we do to help, boys?" she asks, and they tell you the only thing left is starting the fire.

"You get it going," she says to you, "and I'll get firewood with everyone else."

"No problem," you say, and Ali and the others spread out into the canyon, their bodies only barely visible in the gathering gloom, the sound of their laughter echoing through the canyon. You watch them for a while, thinking how much you love these people, and how unfair it would be to lose this. Long after you cannot see them you can still make out the spark and glow of their flashlight beams, blinking like ship's lights in a stormy sea, and you feed paper to the small flame of the fire you've started, a homing beacon for their safe return.

It turned out to be bigger than they thought. The emptiness that ate through the middle ear was one-sixteenth of an inch away from your brain. You are doped up on morphine and aren't really sure what the doctor is talking about, but your parents are there, and they are crying again, and if the surgeon had waited one more week to operate, you might have been dead. Dead or paralyzed, which even in your stupor you know are exactly the same thing. Lying there over the next few days, and then lying at home in your own bed, you think of all the times you have avoided crippled people. You think of the girl who graduated high school a year before you and for whom there was a plaque on the English office wall, who had gone for a drive with her quarterback boyfriend and got in an accident and wasn't the same person when she came out of the coma, couldn't even remember her own name. Before the accident, she had been the star of the school with a full ride to Stanford. You think how you revered that girl, with her raspberry lipstick and denim miniskirts, and how, after the accident, you couldn't even look at her when you passed her wheelchair in the hall. You think of the girl in your seventh grade choir class with lesions all over her body, some sort of auto-immune disease that for the longest time you thought was leprosy, how one day you passed her on your way out of class and she stumbled and grabbed your hand, and how you pulled away from her and ran to the bathroom and got sick in the trashcan, and how you could never tell anyone about it because you knew it was wrong to feel the way you felt.

Most of all, you wish you could let yourself tell him. The two of you lie together on top of your unzipped sleeping bags, a few hundred yards from the rest of the group. The sun is setting, and you watch it drop away over the wall of the canyon.

"Listen," Sean says, so you do, and hear a series of notes that start high then go lower, like a pebble of music bouncing down the canyon walls.

"Canyon wren," he says. "You'll never see them, they're so shy. But sometimes when you're hiking it seems like they're following you, because the song just goes on and on."

You wait to hear it again but there is only silence.

You want to tell him, but right now he is holding your hand in his larger one and tracing your fingers with his thumb. You want to tell him, but you don't want him to see the scar behind your ear or touch the spot back there that feels like a bruised peach, don't want him to pull away. You want to tell him but you don't, because his vision of you is your vision of yourself, and as long as he thinks you are perfect then you are.

The worst thing is that it might not really be gone and there is no way for you to know. It could be growing back even now. Recurring, as the doctor says, and you picture disease spreading through your head like ripples from a stone thrown in a pond. You find yourself thinking of the word at odd moments, when you are driving, or hiking, or sitting in class. Recur recur recur recur, you make the word smaller and smaller in your mind like a fading echo, saying it so many times it becomes nothing more than a bunch of sounds slamming against one another before they disappear.

No matter how dry it seems, the river leaves its mark on the canyon. The water is a narrow green ribbon, and the bushes and rocks covered with moss mark out a path you are to follow. Like rings on tree trunks, you can distinguish wet years from dry in the layers of algae at a puddle's edge.

When you round a bend to find the biggest pool you've seen so far, Ben is the first to jump in. He gives a single glance at the twenty-foot drop and the olive green water below, backs up a few feet, and with a running leap disappears over the edge. You listen to his shout for what seems like minutes, and then to a distant splash.

"*Shiiiiiit*," Sean says, his voice full of admiration. You think glumly to yourself that that will be the last you see of Ben, that even if he survived the jump he won't be able to climb back up, that he should have at least thrown a rock over the edge first to see how long it took to fall. In the time it takes you to transplant Ben into the memorial service you had imagined for yourself a few months before, he swims to the side of the pool and shouts up at you from below.

"It's amazing," he says. "Transcendent. You all have to do it."

It takes no more coaxing than this. Sean, annoyed that he wasn't the first to jump, follows Ben over the edge, his loud whoop echoing over the water. Then Ali, jelly shoes and all, takes her own running leap and disappears from view, her scream high and reckless and full of joy.

Soon everyone has jumped but you. They jump with style, with grace, cannonballing out from the edge and doing twists in the air, their only goal to jump farther or better than the person who went before. You sit down on an overhanging rock and stare down at the specks of them in the water beneath you.

Think of erosion. Think of your skull, your bones, as rock, and think of the tumor as water. It makes sense this way. At first the rock is strong, but water is persistent, and before long little pieces wash away.

Think of surgery as the creation of a dam, struts and ballasts holding back the water's flow. Think of how dams burst, how water's power released can erase whole towns, how the pressure is strongest at the point of the break.

Of course you have to do it. You cannot just sit on the rock and wave back at them. The problem, or one of the problems, is that you can't just drop; you actually have to leap out in order to land in the right place. But your toes are curled around the edge of the rock like claws, and your body doesn't feel strong enough to survive the fall. You picture the hole in your head filled with water and sinking like a stone.

Twenty minutes pass, and everyone except for Sean has gotten out of the water to sit at the edge of the pool and wait for you.

"I'll catch you," he yells.

You start to cry. You feel your legs moving beneath you, and you are running towards the edge, thinking that no matter what else happens, for the minute you are falling you will be just like them. But you are silent and unsmiling as you plunge through the air, and when you smack into the water it is colder than you would have thought. Your head goes under and you open your eyes to look up at the surface as you descend, the darkening water rippling away from the disturbance your body has created. ❧

The Absolute Worst Thing

Seth Carey

Ever since kindergarten, I'd wait at the school bus stop with my best friend Chris Kelly. To kill the time we'd invent games. 'The absolute worst thing' was a real favorite. We'd dream up the worst situations we could think of and progressively build upon them until they were as dreadful as possible.

No matter how we tried to outdo it, the absolute worst we could come up with was always trumped by one particular scenario:

"What if you could still think and feel but you weren't able to move?"

We agreed—this was The Absolute Worst Thing.

That was about thirty years ago, and I still think it's the absolute worst thing.

I was diagnosed with Lou Gehrig's Disease (ALS) December 14, 2001—no problem remembering that date. The doctors who diagnosed me were careful to explain that this meant a death sentence. I was thirty-nine years old.

When they suggested one more blood test, since "maybe you're lucky and you just have AIDS," I knew that the absolute worst thing was for real, and it was happening to me. I knew things were going to get ugly, so I told my good friend (and recent girlfriend), Shannon, that she should run from me. Luckily for me she ignored sound advice and asked to get married instead.

We got married that March.

In the last two years, seven months, and eight days, this disease I'd never heard of has been busy kicking my ass. I've gathered way too much info on ALS (all of it depressing) and can rattle on about it. It boils down to this: ALS kills motor neurons, the signal pathways to voluntary muscles. Those are what you use for things you want to do, like petting the cat, rolling over in bed, holding your head up…you get the idea.

Those muscles are also used in breathing, something I do regularly, and very much hope to keep on doing.

I have bulbar onset ALS, whose symptoms include uncontrollable outbursts of laughter and weeping, sometimes both at once. Fortunately for me, most of my outbursts have been in the more socially acceptable form of laughter. The slightest humorous thought, or the dreaded heart-tug of a Spielberg moment, so popular in phone commercials, and I wave goodbye to self-composure. It makes it tough to act macho. It's not as bad as it was initially but I still cry in my oatmeal most mornings.

I miss being able to do everything I used to do. I thought I understood what I'd miss and could sort of stockpile experiences to keep from missing them too much. It worked better with some things than with others.

I knew that I'd miss fishing, so I did a butt-load of it. But how can you stock up on hugging your wife?

We have three cats I can no longer pet. Shannon, my wife, sometimes takes my hand and runs it over the fur of one that's nearby. The cats start purring and, usually, I end up sobbing.

Mosquito season has now become its own special form of torture. I watch the mosquitoes land on me. They walk about a bit searching for just the right spot to drill. I try to explain to whomever is around, what's happening. My voice is hard to understand in the best circumstances, but when you add frustration and impending doom, I'm reduced to undecipherable yowls. They only know I'm upset, but not why.

I know all too well there's nothing funny about ALS. It's stripped me of the use of my body and voice. It has been an endless source of frustration and humiliation.

But there's already enough depressing crap written about ALS. Laughter and denial are the tools that make living with this nightmare possible.

I credit my approach to dealing with ALS to the many hours I've spent stuck in highway traffic. When you find yourself in a traffic jam, you are faced with a choice. You can get all mad, flipping the finger to everyone, banging on the dashboard. Or you put on your favorite CD, rummage around for a roach, and sing along with the guitar solo.

Either way you're going to end up at the same place. &

What the MRI Doesn't Show

Katherine Riegel

On the phone my sister says
she's stuck in all directions,
and I imagine a starfish cursed
with a mind in each leg
and no desire the same.
But that's not quite accurate—
it's more like some winged thing
held in place with glue,
and that glue is her injured
brain, shaken inside the skull
three times like a ripe peach
in a glass jar.
                           The first time
she was sixteen and jumping
the horse I loved best;
he could not help
that she was under
him when he fell. So much of
what we said was just who she was—
late, disorganized, messy,
no sense of direction—
may be no more an inherent part
of her personality than having three legs
is the natural form of the cat
my father's girlfriend adopted.
I don't know, though I was nine
when it happened and should
remember.
                           The others
were this past year, two car accidents
in the ice of a Boulder winter.
For a while she carried her mail
around in her purse,
unable to decide what she should do

about the bills, bank statements,
solicitations for money and sympathy.
Sounds hit her like fists. Complex
visual patterns—paisley or traffic—become nets
to entangle her. But when she sends
me a letter to edit for her
the clear, thoughtful prose sweeps
me up, her deep compassion a throbbing
rhythm under the leggiero phrasing,
and I realize how fine an instrument
she still has, and enough music
to save or break
her into pieces, trying to get out.

ɞ

The Dress

Joy Rhoades

Cowan, New South Wales, Summer 1974

Bernadette Mobbs hand-sews the wedding dress's zipper in place. She is a big woman, nearing fifty, and she wears her usual long-sleeved blouse buttoned at the wrists and neck above a large elasticized skirt that reaches almost to her ankles. Tucking the needle for safekeeping into an obvious fold, she frees a pudgy hand to pat with a washer the sweat collecting below the tight permed curls on the back of her neck.

Emma Franson appears in the doorway leading from the narrow front verandah.

"Mrs. Mobbs, Macca's here. My fiancé. Can I introduce you?" Emma is almost 30, just 5 feet tall, square-framed and toned from work on her parents' cattle place.

Mrs. Mobbs follows the girl along the narrow front verandah, and down the steps. She stops and turns to push the loose top step back in place, flush with the house. "How do ya do." The man on the other side of the fence pulls off his John Deere cap. He is rangy, a mullet and ear stud at odds with conservative bone-colored trousers and elasticized boots, the uniform of local cattlemen.

Mrs. Mobbs nods. "She's chosen a beautiful pattern."

Macca glances at Emma. Mrs. Mobbs knows the local consensus is that, at her age, Emma is lucky to catch Macca, even if he is a bit of a lout. The gossip has it that he's overlooked her plainness, as he's set his sights on her parents' property.

"Interesting lawn job." Macca grins and Mrs. Mobbs is embarrassed.

"My husband Tony always cuts it low to slow it coming back." She leans down to pull away weeds that have sprouted from a garden ornament, a swan made from an old tire. The white paint has peeled away, revealing the tread.

"Maybe your old man should put that bird out of its misery," Macca suggests. The swan's neck hangs at an odd angle to the ground, bent by the hot sun or by a child jumping on it once too often, or both.

By habit, Mrs. Mobbs lifts the swan's head off the ground and tries to straighten the neck. When she takes her hand away, the head drops back to the ground.

Back in her sewing room, Mrs. Mobbs helps Emma into the partly sewn wedding dress. Inside out, it is held together with pins, making her customer look like a poorly wrapped gift. The stiff cream silk does not flow but dents and puckers to hold each knock, a physical history of the wearer's moves.

An occasional gust of rottenness in the limp breeze carries through the sewing room. An easterly spreads the stench from the town's meat works, always worse in the hot weather.

Mrs. Mobbs is pinning a sleeve seam when she stops. Both she and Emma look down at the three neat round spots bruised in a haphazard semi-circle, just above Emma's elbow. Mrs. Mobbs turns to search through the packets on her cutting table. She holds up a piece of the material from which the gown is cut. "I have enough. I can make longer sleeves."

"But there's no need. The wedding's three weeks away. And long sleeves will be too hot in this heat," Emma replies. Mrs. Mobbs puts the material on the shelf above the sewing machine.

A few days later, the hot afternoon stillness of the house is broken by the dual thumps of a tennis ball thrown against the back wall. Mrs. Mobbs looks up from the half-made dress on her lap. Hearing another noise, she lifts the dress from her lap across onto the cutting table. Her tread is soft along the corridor that forms the spine of the house, her breathing labored.

"Shane?"

She pushes the verandah screen door ajar. Strong summer sunlight forces her to shade her eyes.

"Shane."

She sees her skinny twelve-year-old start at her curt tone, a cricket-bat in his hands. He looks at her through glasses held together with tape at the bridge of his nose, his white-blonde hair cut close. He's kicked off his school shoes and socks somewhere, but still wears the gray shirt and shorts of the town's only primary school. A tennis ball rolls away from his feet and off the edge of the landing into the dead grass of the garden.

"You'll wake your father," says Mrs. Mobbs.

"He's on the late shift?" he almost whispers.

"Yes. Now quick sticks! Go and play at the Cootes."

Shane lays the bat down and nudges it with his foot under the bench, forcing it in among broken racquets and ping-pong bats. He jumps from the landing to the dirt and is gone.

Spreading dust, a whirly-wind gusts across the backyard, tossing paper and leaves about. Mrs. Mobbs pulls the screen door shut behind her and walks back along the corridor, pausing outside the bedroom to listen. On the wall hang three green plastic ducks, each higher than the next, the lowest askew. She reaches out to straighten it, then walks back to the sewing room.

Two weeks later, Emma arrives on time for her second-to-last fitting. After washing her hands, she strips off her riding boots and jeans to put on the dress. Mrs. Mobbs checks the bodice. She moves up from the girl's hip to her waist to her armpit, pinning where adjustment is needed at precise intervals of three-quarters of an inch for a careful, accurate fit. She reaches Emma's left underarm. This time the bruises run around the girl's arm.

"I'll put in new sleeves." The words are muffled, as Mrs. Mobbs' lips hold pins, sharp end out. Her focus is on the sleeve; to replace it will take several hours, but she has time. Emma's eyes move from her arm to the gown's unsewn hem.

Mrs. Mobbs pulls a small wooden box from under the cutting table and places it on the cracked lino next to Emma, just beyond the sweep of the dress's skirt. She helps Emma onto the box.

Emma has chosen tiny cream bows for the skirt. They need to be pinned and sewn by hand. To position the bows, Mrs. Mobbs kneels on one knee like a bulky suitor. Emma begins shifting her weight from one foot to the other.

"Try to keep still. Won't be long now."

But the skirt continues to shift about. Mrs. Mobbs looks up and sees Emma is crying. To stop tears falling on the gown, Mrs. Mobbs stands and places a towel around Emma's neck like a bib.

"I don't know why he does it." Emma's voice is low. Mrs. Mobbs lifts packets of material, searching for her tissues.

"Do your parents know?" She pulls the tissue box out from under some unhemmed curtains and offers them to Emma, who takes one.

"No. We don't talk much now. Since I moved in with Macca. They just want us to get married." Emma blows her nose and her eyes settle on her arms. She begins to cry again. "Will he stop?" she asks. "Once we're married?"

Mrs. Mobbs fiddles with the bodice seam, and turns away to get more pins. She waits for the tears to stop before she resumes pinning.

After Emma leaves, Mrs. Mobbs works on the dress. The sewing machine whine rises and falls with her push and release of the pedal.

"Bugger," she swears. She has caught a fold of the bodice material in a seam and will have to use care unpicking to avoid leaving thread marks on the gown.

Distracted, she puts the dress aside. She might have nicked the bodice, a serious and expensive error, and something she cannot afford so close to the wedding day. She goes to the hot semi-darkness of the kitchen and puts the kettle on.

Sitting at the table, arms folded, cigarette in the fingers of her right hand, she hears the kettle shrieking for some time before it prompts her to move. She turns off the stove and finds there is only just enough water for the tea. She half-fills the teapot and leans against the kitchen counter, waiting for the tea to brew, thinking.

She pours the tea and returns to sit at the table, fanning herself. This heat, so late in the day, means there may be rain later. She feels drops of perspiration slide down under her armpits and slow as they reach the mounds of flesh at her waist.

Balancing her cigarette on a chipped ashtray, she unbuttons each cuff to cool down just for a minute, folding up each sleeve until they reach just above her elbows, her skin cooling with the unaccustomed exposure.

She looks down at her own forearms, resting on the table, then lifts and rotates each in turn, to check. There is not much to see. This gives her pause: those that fade will be replaced. She has been very careful—but supposes one or two people have put two and two together over the years. She feels a flush of shame.

She is uncomfortable; she does not usually see herself as a thinker. There is no good in it—there is nowhere she and Shane could go. And he has never touched Shane. She takes care not to mull over things too much. She learned that early on. If she thinks too much, she gets sad. And her husband doesn't like her to be sad.

The screen door bangs, and she automatically folds down her sleeves and buttons her cuffs, relieved to be interrupted.

"Hi." Shane slings his school port onto the kitchen floor, and sits.

Mrs. Mobbs gets up to pour him some cordial. "Want a biccie?" she asks, wrestling the tight lid off the tin. He takes two and grins at her.

"Dad home?" Shane asks, his mouth full. She shakes her head. He puts a foot up on a kitchen chair. She taps it away with her hand.

They sit and he hums while munching, flipping through a Spiderman comic. She watches him closely.

"Hullo Mrs. M. I have to be quick—Macca's waiting," Emma, almost out of breath, greets Mrs. Mobbs. Unprompted, Emma washes her hands. Mrs. Mobbs helps her into the dress. It takes time for Mrs. Mobbs to fasten the faux pearl buttons that run down the gown's back. Each must be nudged into its own handmade loop.

"Turn around. Have a look," Mrs. Mobbs motions to the mirror on the wall behind the girl. Emma grabs two large handfuls of skirt. She turns and releases them; a tentative smile appears on her face. Smoothing the front of the skirt, she erases the puckers that have gathered.

"It's beautiful." She looks at Mrs. Mobbs, who is on her knees pulling the small train out at the back of the gown for best effect. Mrs. Mobbs heaves herself off one knee, back to a standing position and admires the result. Emma is almost beautiful, the gentle lines of the dress softening her angular workaday self.

"Thank you." Emma continues to look at her own reflection.

"Emma," Mrs. Mobbs begins, then looks down at the train. "Last time… you asked me."

Emma cuts her off. "Oh, it's all right. I was just going on."

"Yes, but," Mrs. Mobbs says, but stops when a car horn startles them both. Emma looks towards the front door.

"Can you unhook me? I've got to get going." She picks up fistfuls of skirt and backs towards Mrs. Mobbs, waiting. Emma turns towards her.

"Mrs. M—can you undo me?"

Emma looks at her. "Mrs. Mobbs?" She reaches out and touches the woman's elbow. "The buttons. Can you undo them?"

Her fingers slow, Mrs. Mobbs unfastens the buttons one by one. Emma wriggles her arms out of the long sleeves and leans forward for Mrs. Mobbs to lift the dress off over her shoulders.

Mrs. Mobbs coaxes the dress into a plastic cover and Emma tugs on her top and skirt. Emma pulls a crumpled check from her pocket and hands it over.

"Thanks again," she says, squeezing Mrs. Mobbs' hands.

The horn sounds twice, extended blasts. Emma scoops up the dress in its plastic cover on her way out onto the front verandah.

Mrs. Mobbs follows her out and calls to her. Emma stops at the fence, waiting. Mrs. Mobbs is puffing when she reaches Emma and she breathes in to attempt to speak, but says nothing. Reaching out to take Emma's hand, she tries again, but no words come. Emma smiles and climbs into the waiting ute.

Mrs. Mobbs watches the cloud of dust thrown up by Macca's wheels waft across the intersection. She leans her elbows on the fence as the dust drifts, then settles. When the car is out of sight, she drags the gate shut and walks slowly back into the house. ❧

Pill

Colleen Abel

Go ahead, take it.
        It will put out the fire that kept you

up nights writing and writing, it will silence
        the chatter inside that kept you

from sleeping. Days will be flat
        and familiar as your beloved prairie hometown.

Sharp will soften. Tight will loosen.
        Go ahead,

push off toward that opposite shore
        in the forgiving darkness, remember

in Thailand, November, how they send
        their lotus lanterns nodding through shadows

toward the sea, nodding yes—*yes*—
        to that journey.

            ଏ

Shaking the Dead Geranium

Harriet Rzetelny

I was sitting in my office staring at a column of travel expenses when the call came in.

"This is Marushka." Hearing her voice on the phone for the first time, it sounded harsher than I remembered it. "You'd better come. Your brother's very bad."

My stomach lurched. "What happened? What did he do?"

"Just come."

I closed my eyes and took a deep breath. Then I went into Ellen's office and said, "I have to go. It's Ben."

Ellen is a dynamic-looking blond who, at forty, is only a few years older than I. She owns the small but successful consulting firm where I work as her executive assistant. She shot me a look full of questions she knew better than to ask, and said, "Keep me posted, Molly."

Ellen's willingness to let me go when Ben needs me is the main reason I work for her. In return, she gets an efficient, college-educated person who comes in early, stays late, and is willing to work for far less money than she's worth. In the beginning Ellen would invite me out for drinks and was full of curiosity and well-meaning advice. But I've gotten very good at evading people's attempts at friendship. There are so many things I can't talk about, I've learned over the years that it's not worth even getting started, no matter how well-meaning people may be.

The last time I'd seen Ben was two weeks ago. I'd gone to check up on him as I do regularly, especially during these times when his mind loses its mooring and he stops taking care of himself. I'd let myself into his tiny two-room apartment and walked through the cramped kitchen into the bedroom-cum-living room. He was stretched out on the daybed with his back to me and his head on Marushka's voluminous skirt. Marushka, a widow with several grown children, must have once been quite beautiful. She was sitting propped up against the wall, her face framed by a mane of rust-colored hair, like an edging of autumn foliage around a crumbled bouquet. Her neon-purple blouse was open and he had one of her still magnificent breasts in his mouth. Our eyes met; hers were full of defiance. I guess she thought I wouldn't approve.

Marushka was one of a large tribe of Gypsies who lived on the first floor in my brother's Lower East Side tenement building. She was usually out on the stoop when I visited him, and occasionally we passed the time of day. I had never seen her talking to Ben, so I was quite taken aback when I walked in on them. I didn't know why I thought Ben's mental illness had wiped out his sexuality along with his ability to balance a checkbook. I also didn't know how she'd gotten past his pervasive mistrust of people that kept him so isolated, I being the exception. But I was grateful he had a connection with somebody, anybody other than me, and that he was getting at least a modicum of pleasure in life.

Ben was eight years older than I, tall, with hair that curled tightly around his head and a hawk's nose always poking into something. When we were younger, Ben had been my friend and protector, my buffer against the world. But that was before the illness began ravaging his brain. Back then, the spotlight of my mother's love had focused on him, the brilliant son; she had little to spare for me, the quiet child, nor for my father who had finally stopped coming home. I kept hoping she would discover in my secret self something unique and special to love; it never seemed to happen. She died ten years ago from lung cancer, still mourning the son she'd lost, hardly aware of the daughter who sat dutifully at her bedside.

Ben was dazzling and fierce. He fought my fights for me and taught me how to look beyond the surface and see beauty. I adored him. By age sixteen, he'd won awards for his poetry and a full scholarship to Emory College. By the end of his eighteenth year, he'd had his first psychotic episode: convinced that my mother was sucking the life fluids out of his brain, he went after her with a bread knife. By thirty he'd been hospitalized three more times. He was now forty-three. He never graduated from Emory. He never held a job, published a book, fathered a child. Between hospitalizations, he lived as a minimally functional, oddly brilliant, but always reclusive eccentric; a kind of semi-life made possible by modern pharmacology.

All the men in my life—with the exception of my brother—come and go rather quickly. One of the men I dated briefly once asked me where it was written that I had to be Ben's mother. I couldn't explain it to him; my feelings about Ben are only a part of the story. I was the one who called 911 that first time, when Ben tried to attack our mother. I was ten years old. After the police wrestled him to the ground, and he was chained up like a dog and carried, kicking and screaming, out of the house, I locked myself in my room and cried for so long that the doctor had to give me a sedative. After that, my mother faded away, little by little. Mostly I remember her hunched over the kitchen table, cigarette in hand, playing solitaire. The doctors diagnosed it as depression, but I knew what it really was. The one person she truly loved had hated her so much he tried to kill her. She never forgave me for making that call, for telling the world about it, although I don't know what she thought I should have done.

That day—my brother's murderous attack and my revelation of it—lives in me like a jagged wound that won't heal. It was so gut-wrenching for both Ben and me, that it forged an unbreakable bond between us and he's come to rely on me as the one constant in his otherwise erratic existence.

After that, I took a vow of silence. I'd betrayed my mother once and I would never do it again. Throughout my childhood, I found it easier to say nothing than to possibly say the wrong thing. And her death hasn't changed that fact. It's left me isolated and pretty much alone, except for Ben. Fortunately, I truly like my brother and enjoy spending time with him—when he's not actively psychotic. His mind is like an old suit of once-excellent quality, that has been patched and re-patched with odd pieces of material that don't quite go together, kind of like a crazy quilt. Some people might think it belongs in the rag bin. But not me. I've always been drawn to the odd and unusual in life, and I find Ben's mind endlessly fascinating.

The next time I tried to visit Ben, after the primal scene I'd witnessed between him and Marushka the week prior, he was out, probably on one of his long rambling walks. I knocked on Marushka's door and thanked her for being kind to him. Her eyes flashed, undoubtedly at my choice of words. I realized then how hungry I was for someone I could talk to about him, someone who already knew him and needed no explanations, and who might understand what it means to love him. But she didn't have much to say, or if she did, she wasn't going to share it with me. I scribbled down my phone numbers and told Marushka to call if Ben ever got to be too much for her. She took the scrap of paper and tucked it somewhere inside her blouse.

I wasn't really surprised when she called. It's always just a matter of time. But it was the tone of her voice that made the decision for me. I took a deep breath and dialed Tony Baretti. He was the intake social worker at Marble Heights, the small, private hospital in suburban Westchester where I decided to hospitalize Ben, if and when the time came. Tony had been the speaker at one of the many group meetings for families of the mentally ill I'd attended over the years, and we became friends—sort of. At least I trusted him. And he did share my amusement at some of Ben's wilder delusions—such as the one in which he decoded a fortune cookie that told him Billy Collins, our little known Poet Laureate at the time, had blown up the World Trade Center to prove that poetry still mattered. Also, Tony doesn't tell me I need to get a life.

As I waited for Tony to answer, I began to hope that I was over-reacting. Maybe I had read the signs wrong. Or Marushka had. Or something. But I didn't want a repeat of that terrible first time. Or the ones after that. Altogether, Ben had been hospitalized five times. Each time he'd been taken by the police to a city psych ward. The last one was a horror show. The building looked like a fortress and the entranceway into the unit was through a dark, narrow corridor with filthy, scuffed walls that smelled like the public bathroom in a bus station. Someone—one of the inmates, I supposed, but it could easily have been one of the staff—kept screaming "I'm not gonna take it anymore" over and over again, until I was afraid I'd start screaming myself.

Tony finally answered and I explained the situation.

"Perhaps he needs to have his medication adjusted," Tony said. "Has anyone been following him in aftercare?"

"Ben's stopped taking his medication," I said. "The most recent one they gave him was fogging his brain out so much he insisted they were shooting guacamole in through his ears."

"Okay," Tony said, as though guacamole in the ears was a normal, everyday occurrence. "We'll get the paperwork started."

My resolve evaporated again. "Maybe he doesn't really need it yet. Maybe I should try to reach the psychiatrist at the aftercare center." But I didn't even know who the current psychiatrist was—they flitted in and out of the center like fireflies on a hot summer evening. The last one I'd met, who was gone now, had been a young, well-meaning Pakistani who viewed Ben's long, rambling discourses which were full of historical, philosophical, and poetic references as a symptom that needed to be extinguished by increased medication. He didn't understand that these discourses were all that remained of my brother's once fine mind; destroy them, and you leave him with nothing but his illness.

"Molly," Tony said gently. "I know this is hard for you." When I didn't say anything, he went on: "I wish you would talk to me a little more."

Oh Tony, I thought, sometimes I wish I could, too. But the habit of silence is so hard to break. The words just disappear off my tongue like snowflakes melting on my hand.

"Well," he sighed, "it will all be in the works if you decide to bring him here. But remember that this is a private hospital, which means *you'll* have to get him here. City cops won't bring him."

"I know, Tony. But Ben hates hospitals."

"It's a tough call, Molly. But if you let him go without help too long, it'll be worse for both of you." When I didn't respond he said, "Well, if you don't do it now and he gets really bad, you may just have to let the police take him in to one of the local hospitals. Maybe after he's stabilized a little, we can have him transferred."

No, I thought, the images of his earlier commitments in the city hospitals flashing through my mind like scenes from the theater of the damned. Not that. "I'm going over there now. I'll let you know."

A thin afternoon sun filtered down from the autumn sky as I climbed the stairs from the subway and turned the corner onto Ben's block. The run-down tenements lining the street leaned into each other like a row of old alkies trying to hold each other up. Marushka stood outside the building waiting for me, her arms hugging her chest. She wore a thin sweater over a low-cut blouse, and was shivering a little in the chilly air.

"Couple days ago, he came into my apartment and started accusing me of being the devil's harlot," she began before I could get my mouth open. "When I yelled at him to get out, he got wild, threw a lamp at the wall, made a hole as big as a soup bowl. Now why does he want to go and do that?" Two curved lines, like parentheses, appeared above her eyes. "Niclos had to chase him out with a baseball bat." Niclos was the brother of her dead husband. "He's been locked in his bedroom since then. He won't come out or answer me. I don't think he's eaten. I hear him mumbling through the door. Niclos is up there."

"Oh, Marushka, I'm so sorry," I said, wishing I could just shake some sense into my crazy brother. "Of course, I'll pay for any damages."

I'd genuinely wanted to take Ben's relationship with Marushka as a sign that maybe the slow, steady decline of the past couple of months was miraculously reversing. I was always ready for a miracle. I searched for positive indications in his behavior and appearance. Failing that, I pounced on his daily horoscope for possible portents in the stars. I didn't want to have to hospitalize him.

Now I was angry at him; despite his fear and terror of hospitals, he was incapable of staying at least minimally sane. And I was angry at myself because my love was inadequate to protect him, as if love could be equated with some amulet—a cross, a Star of David, a crystal. I knew this was irrational. Chemicals were exploding in his brain and blowing out his synapses. The power or potency of my love couldn't change that. But I felt as though it should.

I called Ellen on my cell phone to tell her I'd need the rest of the day off, and then started up the stairs with Marushka following me. The door to Ben's apartment was open and Niclos was standing in the kitchen, baseball bat in hand. He watched us come in without saying anything, but his face clearly said, "You're both crazier than he is for not putting him away a long time ago." Remembering the force of Ben's terror-driven rages, I was just grateful Niclos was there.

The bedroom door was closed. I knocked gently and tried to turn the knob. It was locked. "Ben, it's me, Molly. Please let me in."

Nothing.

I knocked again, a little harder. "I'm worried about you, Ben. I just want to see that you're okay."

"The voices are coming in through the walls." Ben's voice. "The walls are the stalls where they keep the words. Molly it's not. It's the words of the voices that say Molly, but how can you know evil from the mouth of a sister?"

My heart, hammering in my chest, pounded so loud I wondered if Ben could hear it through the door. "Ben, I don't want you to be hurt. Please just open the door."

"I can only live by dying."

"He's been talking a lot about dying," Marushka whispered sharply. I hadn't even realized she was behind me. I could see this was no easy decision for her, either. "Niclos can break the door down," she said, her voice catching a little. "Maybe you better call the police."

No. Not the police. "I'll be back soon," I said to Marushka and hurried down the stairs.

Instead of going home, turning off the phone and burrowing under the covers, which was what I felt like doing, I headed towards a car rental agency I'd noticed on the main street, a couple of blocks away. After signing what seemed like an endless number of papers, I picked up a car and drove back to my brother's building, pulling up in front of a no-parking sign. Two older black men sat on the next stoop arguing with each other and drinking wine out of a bag-wrapped bottle. They looked up as I got out of the car. The curtain in Marushka's first-floor window flicked, and in a moment she was out of her door and following me up the stairs. Niclos, still holding his baseball bat, sat on a chair in Ben's kitchen. Everything in the room was black, including the sink, the refrigerator, the stove, and the window—a kind of tenement Hades. Or the eternal midnight of a lost mind. The only spot of non-black was a dying geranium in a small green plastic pot on the windowsill, its drooping flowers the color of old, dried blood.

Midnight shakes the memory as a madman shakes a dead geranium. Who wrote that? My brother, the madman, was always flinging lines of poetry around as if they were perfectly reasonable explanations for his irrational behaviors. I took a yoga breath to calm the trickle of anxiety that always hit me in the stomach whenever I behaved in any way that might be an indication that I, too, could be crazy. I knocked on his bedroom door again. "Ben, it's me, Molly. Please let me in."

Nothing.

"So should I tell Niclos to break the door down?" Marushka whispered.

"No," I whispered back. "That would frighten him even more."

"So what are you gonna do?"

I thought for a minute. "There's a fire escape around back. Maybe I can get in that way and talk to him."

We retraced our steps down to the first floor. The hallway stank from old garbage and the unwashed bodies and stale urine of homeless people who used the stairwell for shelter. The back door leaned crazily on one hinge. I went out into a rear courtyard full of stained mattresses, abandoned furniture, and discarded food containers.

Ben lived on the third floor, which meant climbing up two flights. I wondered briefly whether the rusted, crumbling fire escape would hold me. Then I forced myself to think about the dozens of neighborhood burglars who used these fire escapes, quite successfully, as their personal accessways.

By the time I reached Ben's landing, I was filthy from the grime and flakes of rust. I wiped my hands on my skirt and looked in the window. Ben was sitting barefoot on the floor in half-lotus position, surrounded by burning candles, like someone about to be sacrificed in a primitive ritual. I was shocked at how old his body looked—stooped and scrawny—although it was only two weeks since I'd seen him last. When had his hair gotten so gray? He was dressed bizarrely—never a good sign—in a checked shirt and dirty striped pants. An old orange beach towel, patterned with a big starfish in the middle, was tied with a cord around his waist. He sat watching the door, so he didn't notice me out on the fire escape.

The wooden window frame was so rotted I could easily have removed it, but a metal gate covered the window. Without any real hope I pulled it and, wonder of wonders, it slid open; my paranoid brother had forgotten to lock it, another sign of his increasing derangement.

As I was attempting to slide the window frame out of its track, the glass suddenly came out in my hand and went tumbling down into the courtyard below. At the sound, Ben shot his head around, his face shiny with terror. We stared at each other, and for a moment I could see the scene through his eyes: some filthy apparition who had taken on the visage of his sister was trying to climb through his window to do God knows what to him.

I felt a quick stab of fear; after all, I knew full well what he was capable of. But, I reminded myself, in all the years of his madness, he'd never tried to hurt me. At least, not so far. I just had to convince him that I was who I said I was.

"Ben, it's me, Molly." I tried to smile. "I climbed up the fire escape because you wouldn't let me in. That's why I look so dirty." It sounded lame, even to me.

Ben yanked two candles off the floor where they had been attached by, I assumed, melted wax and sprang up to face me, a candle poised like a fiery sword in each hand.

"Ben," I said, trying to sound enticing and a little mischievous, "I have a car. Remember how much fun we used to have when Daddy would take us for car rides? Put down the candles and let's go for a ride."

"The lies shine through your evil eyes," he said, jabbing the candles toward me.

I should have known that lying to him was not the way to go—he was too smart. I searched my mind frantically for some way to calm his fears and convince him of who I was.

"Do you remember the song you used to sing to me when I was a little girl and would have nightmares?" I began to sing:

> Rock-a-bye, don't you cry
> Go to sleepy little baby.
> When you wake, you shall have
> All the pretty little horses.

The candles wavered and he thrust his head forward to peer at me, as if a tiny flicker of recognition might have penetrated his psychotic haze. Not because I knew the words to the childhood song—an evil imposter would certainly know that—but because I sang it in the atonal, off-key voice that he'd always teased me about.

"Ben, I want to get you some help, so you'll be safe." My voice sounded eerie and hollow to me, like a ghostly echo in an empty house. "I'm worried about you and I love you. You're my big brother." As I said the words, I suddenly felt them so powerfully that my body began to shake. I grabbed the sill so I wouldn't fall off the fire escape.

By now, he was staring at me intently. I knew him so well that I could almost read what was going on inside his head, or I thought I could. He was desperately trying to hang onto whatever ability he still had to distinguish what was actually happening from the jumble of voices in his head that were telling him crazy things. Was I really Molly? It must have been terrifying for him not to know.

"Ben, if you just come with me, I promise not to let anyone hurt you." I hoped it was a promise I could keep. "If you won't come, I'm going to have to call for help."

I never got to find out whether or not he understood me because at that moment a blob of hot wax plopped onto his bare foot.

He jumped back and dropped the candle. As he did, the candle in his other hand went out. I climbed in through the window, murmuring in a gentle voice, the way you would calm a frightened animal.

"Come on, Ben," I said. "Come with me. You can take your candles with you if you want. Marushka and Niclos are in the kitchen. I'm going to tell them to move away." The words from one of the Family Skills group meetings I'd attended flooded into my mind: approach gently, but with assurance. Tell the patient exactly what you are going to do before you do it.

Ben's eyes were full of suspicion as he tried to plot the plots that would protect him from a world he could no longer cope with. But after stooping down to pick up an unlighted candle, he straightened up and moved in my direction. I knew better than to try and touch him. I simply murmured in the same calm voice, "That's right, Ben. Come with me." I could almost smell the fear radiating from him, but I could also see the lines of strain running down his face. He wasn't nineteen anymore; perhaps he was just too tired to fight anymore. Whatever it was, he let me lead him to the bedroom door.

I unlocked it, gave him a reassuring smile and said, "Marushka and Niclos, please move back. My brother and I are going out for a little while." I shot a quick glance over my shoulder. Ben was watching Niclos and the baseball bat like a child watching the closet where he knows the bogeyman is hiding. Continuing to murmur reassurances at him, I stood back and allowed him to precede me through the kitchen door and out of the apartment.

When we got to the stairs he stopped. I waved him on, wondering if he would bolt. But where could he go? Niclos and the baseball bat were in back of him. He started down the stairs with me trailing along behind him like the rear guard. We must have made a strange spectacle—Ben in his bare feet and his ridiculous beach towel, still clutching his candle, and I, the filthy betrayer with bits of rust clinging to her clothes. I was still trying to convince myself that I was doing the right thing, still telling myself that he would never hurt me. All the while I continued to murmur calm reassurances at him.

Everything was moving along until we got onto the street. I don't know whether Ben had planned all along that it would be easier to get away from me once we were out of the apartment, or whether the noise and activity on the street were just too much for him, but he gave a yell and started running up the block, his skinny legs pumping as hard as they could under the flapping of his orange beach towel.

Like a fool, I stood there and shouted, "Ben, come back!"

"Girl." One of the two elderly wine drinkers looked up at me with a big grin on his face. "Man don' want you? Find one who do. Plenty of us around." The other old man laughed, slapped his bony knee, shook his head and said, "You listen to my man here. He be tellin' you the truth. Don't be chasin' him up no street. Ain't dignified."

But chase him I did. I heard a motor jump into life behind me. A black Lincoln driven by one of Marushka's sons roared past me. Marushka had her family in readiness.

With a screech of brakes, the car pulled up with one wheel on the sidewalk in front of Ben just as he got to the corner, effectively cutting him off. The kid jumped out of the car and rounded the corner so that Ben couldn't run that way. With me coming up behind him, he didn't have too many options besides jabbing at the air with his candle.

Once again, I approached him with gentle reassurance. I guess he decided I was the better of the choices he had right then, because he let me lead him back to the rental car. But his eyes watched me with low cunning.

I heard a *vroom-vroom* and saw the taillights of the Lincoln, now in reverse, pass me as it backed up the block. For a moment, the fear came back and I had a flash of Ben going after my mother with the knife. I pushed the thought away. He won't hurt you. He's never hurt you. He's your brother Ben.

I unlocked the passenger side door of the rental car and told Ben to get in, wondering what I would do if he didn't. To my surprise and relief, he did. I dragged the seat belt over the faded starfish on his beach towel and buckled it as one would do for a small child. My clever brother, however, had been making his plans. By the time I got around the car to get into the driver's seat, he was out of his seat belt, had jerked the door open and was sprinting down the block.

"Some women just can't take no hint." The voice of the first wine drinker.

"Yeah," the reply came. "What you think so turrible 'bout her that he got to get away so badly, can't even wait to put his shoes on?"

The kid was out of the Lincoln and about to tackle Ben by the time I pulled the car around again. Once my big brother would've fought like the devil, but I guess he truly was burning out as he got older, because after I gestured the kid away and said, "Ben, you have to get into the car," he stopped resisting and climbed back into the car. Maybe he'd decided I was really Molly after all.

The trip to Marble Heights went surprisingly smoothly, but my fear was that Ben would open his door and run out into the parkway and there would be no way I could save him.

He didn't. What he did was look at me out of accusing eyes and ramble on about "lying sister words" and a plague of dead rats, dead frogs, and dead vermin that he claimed were crawling around in his body.

As soon as we pulled up in front of the hospital, the accusation in his eyes turned to alarm. Ben had never seen Marble Heights before, and I hadn't mentioned where we were going, but he could spot a mental hospital at one hundred paces anywhere on this earth.

"You go in," he said, shrinking back from me with one of those rare moments of lucidity that are completely unexplainable. "I'll wait here for you."

I coaxed him into the building and murmured reassurances while Tony and the admitting psychiatrist were being paged.

Marble Heights didn't look like your typical psych hospital. It was a low, gray-stoned structure that sat on a beautifully landscaped lawn surrounded by trees and bushes in early autumn shades of yellow and burnished red. The lobby and reception area were carpeted in forest green; the walls were beige with matching green and rose trim and were hung with attractive paintings. Upholstered chairs and low tables with magazines added to the air of quiet normality. But you couldn't fool Ben. His crafty eyes darted around the room as if he was ferreting out the fiend that he knew was hiding behind one of the walls.

Tony was good with Ben, asking his questions in a calm, friendly way and simply accepting Ben's strange and disjointed answers. I'd just begun to relax when a short, dried-up looking man in a starched white coat entered the room.

"I'm Dr. Koster," he said.

His eyes had the slightly bulging look of a toad, and he tended to punctuate his sentences with a clearing of his throat which, unfortunately, gave him a slightly accusatory tone.

"Ehrm! And you are Benjamin Lewin?" he asked. A look of alarm came into Ben's eyes and he stood mute. Not a good start.

"And you are...?" he asked me. I looked down at my filthy, disheveled self and wondered if he was determining whether I, too, was there to be admitted.

Before I could answer, he glanced at the papers in his hands and said, "Molly Lewin, sister."

"I apologize for my appearance," I said. "I had to climb up a fire escape."

He nodded as if this was a perfectly normal occurrence in the lives of his patients' families. Then he turned to my brother. "Hello, Ben," he said in his nasal voice. "I have some questions I'd like to ask you, okay?"

He paused for a minute, but when Ben didn't answer, he went on with the standard list of questions. "When were you born?"

I knew the doctor was trying to assess Ben's mental state, but I also knew how suspicious it would sound to Ben. My brother didn't want people to know the date of his birth because he thought it allowed them to have power over him.

"Birth...the birth of vipers in the raging torrents of the mind battles." As Ben spoke he watched Dr. Koster through narrowed eyes and began to swing his arms back and forth, a sure sign of his increasing agitation.

Dr. Koster stepped back and took a very visible breath. Then he cleared his throat again. "Do you know why you are here?"

Another bad question, one I could have kicked myself for not realizing he would ask. This was, after all, supposed to be a voluntary commitment. Come on Ben, I thought desperately, say something at least halfway normal. But even as the thought crystallized in my brain, I felt a sinking feeling in the pit of my stomach.

Ben stared back at the doctor and started to mutter. He hunched his shoulders forward and his hands became fists. Swinging them, he began to pace around the floor. This interview was going downhill fast.

Dr. Koster turned to Tony and said, "I think we're going to need some back-up to get the patient down on the unit. I'm going to radio for Code Team."

He pulled a small walkie-talkie out of his pocket and spoke into it. Looking back at it later, I realized that the black box with its strange, crackling noises was probably the match that set off the tinderbox. It fed right into Ben's paranoid delusions. Behind me, the Admissions people began to clear out the area: receptionist, visitors, other staff were all being herded away. The hospital was readying itself for the violent outburst from my brother.

And my brother did not disappoint them. He was emitting small, growling noises from his throat which sounded eerily similar to the ones made by the good doctor. The hair on his head stood straight up, as if his terror had set off voltages of electricity in his body which were charging through him like lightening.

As Dr. Koster backed away, he beckoned Tony and me in the direction of the door. "Why don't you take Ms. Lewin into your office?"

Tony took me firmly by the arm. "Come on, Molly. The Crisis Team is trained to deal with Ben. It would just upset you to see this."

"Mind vermin, rats and frogs!" Ben shouted, making a lunge for the walls, banging and kicking against them in his rage to get out. Since he had no shoes on, I was afraid he would break his toes. I wanted to run over and put my arms around him and stop him from destroying himself yet again. But I knew he was over the edge, and that I had become part of the hostile, terrifying world against which he had to protect himself. And there was nothing, nothing, I could do about it.

"Patient rapidly decompensating." Dr. Koster continued talking into the walkie-talkie as he hurriedly left the area. "Seventy-five milligrams of Thorazine, I.M...." The rest was garbled as Tony pulled me away. Four burly men were running up the hall towards us pulling a Reeves stretcher on which to secure the dangerous patient. The Four Horsemen of the Apocalypse. A woman with a stethoscope around her neck trailed after them.

I collapsed into a chair in Tony's office as he ran back to help the staff begin an involuntary commitment of my brother. What I'd been hoping to avoid was happening after all. I had been through enough psych hospitals to know that even in the most private and presentable of them, there would be no carpets and pictures on the walls of the room where they would be taking Ben now. He would be wrapped in a "camisole"—a pretty word for a strait jacket. There would be a mattress on the floor and four bare walls. And he would be alone, screaming in rage at his demons and his terror, until the medication took hold.

The lights were off in the room and I sat staring into space, enveloped in a world of gray fog, hearing and feeling nothing. Gradually I became aware of the slanted rays of light filtering in through the window. For a long time I sat exhausted, demolished, watching the late afternoon sun mute the autumn sprays of yellows and reds on the birches and maples dotting the lawn. The autumnal equinox was past and the sun was low in the sky. On the windowsill in Tony's office stood three pots of geraniums, past their prime, but obviously well-tended. *Midnight shakes the memory as a madman shakes a dead geranium.*

I shuddered, as if a cold wind had suddenly blown through the room. A small pulse started up in the corner of my eye, like the slow beat of a dying heart. Behind the geraniums the leaves drifted lazily down from the trees as if they had all the time in the world to reach the ground. It struck me then that my brother was in the midst of a long, slow autumn, and it wouldn't be long before winter settled in for good. I started to cry, first in giant, gulping sobs and then more quietly, the tears running down my face and off my chin like water dripping from the trees after a heavy rain.

Tony walked into the office. He handed me tissues, waiting patiently until I sopped up my face. The medication had taken hold, he told me. Ben was quiet now and I could visit him. Did I want Tony to come with me?

I said no, I'd be okay. I'd done this lots of times before. Tony told me where to find Ben, and asked me again if I was okay. I nodded. After giving me another quick look, he grabbed his jacket and left.

I sat for a while longer, thinking about my brother. I knew exactly what I would see when I visited him. They would have transferred him to a bed with raised sides, like a metallic crib. He would still be in restraints, his wrists tied to the sides of the bed, and he'd be lying on his back staring up at the ceiling out of vacant eyes. The quirky, sly, fearful, funny, suspicious guardian of the last remnants of his mind—my brother—would not be in that room. My heart was breaking from the loss of him.

You can't bring back the geraniums once they're dead, no matter how much you shake them. Suddenly I saw my life laid out before me, like a diorama in the planetarium: Ben in his crazy paranoid brilliance was the sun, and I was the moon, revolving slowly around him, living in his reflection, with no light of my own. I was thirty-five years old, and the most important relationship I had in my life was with a brother who, on his best days, believed that mad King Ludwig of Bavaria spoke to him through the drainpipe in his sink. Shouldn't I have more than this? Did I still owe my mother the vow of silence I'd taken as a very little girl? Even nuns, dedicated to a life of service, have been known to leave the convent. For a long time I just sat, watching the shadows on the lawn lengthen and flatten until it became so dark I could no longer distinguish their shapes.

Finally I took a deep breath, got up, and walked out into the hall. My heart still felt as though it was breaking, but whether for Ben or for myself I couldn't say. After the gloom of Tony's office, the sudden glare of the fluorescent lights made me blink. It was late and the area was deserted. I should check on Ben and see how he's doing, I thought. But my legs felt heavy, too tired to move. Another poetry fragment, another one of my brother's favorites, came into my mind. *Over the tumbled graves, about the chapel / There is the empty chapel, only the wind's home.* Whichever way I looked, I faced an empty room. Not knowing where to go or what to do, I pulled my coat tightly around my shoulders and walked out into the night. ❧

Lithium and the Absence of Desire

Virginia Chase Sutton

It is not advertised on the pill bottle, merely mentioned
in the product description from the drug store.

You have no idea what you are giving away.
Winter's amnesia is coming. At first it seems impossible

because you live so fully in mossy, rainy lakes. You
have watched pelicans sail over a mirrored surface

just above and just below the water. It is so easy
to shudder beneath a sun as it burns rock to fire over

the island's bumpy landscape. So you drift all the way in,
dozing in light and soaked color. Here you have lived

more than thirty years, as alive as yesterday's romantic boil
of rain and hot skies, the fever popping all along your prickling skin.

You are perfectly at ease in this watery hive. Under the surface
you blur as kisses trail between your open legs.

You are not prepared for the gray clouds stealing close,
shriveling the shoreline to a smudge, sucking at the waves.

Still, you take the medication as prescribed. At first
you imagine your body may adjust or the pills

will come to understand you. It is no use.
Desire falters after the first mouthful, a little

swallow. How you will miss it, the tug and pull
at the body's sweet dampness. You think of escape,

sit in a small boat not far from shore where you eat
pale apricots faded like old wallpaper's delicate skin.

Strain all you will but you have given desire away.
No choice since you must take the pills. The land

contracts and flips over. The medication's flash
freezes you to winter. After time passes, will you remember

the fizz of greenery spilling down embankments,
how you once drank from the lake's clear aluminum?

Back then it was easy to drown in a cup of water,
but this is an unexpected kind of going under.

How you will shiver, forced to settle for icy
ruin, numb winters of regret.

☙

The Devil and a Pocketful of Glass
The Journey of an Obsessive-Compulsive

Craig Boyer

March, 1977. I'm 13. I pray in the dark woods above the city. I pray that I won't have to keep blinking. But the devil whispers: "What if a naked lady pops into your head?"

I blink—I crush that whisper with my eyelids. Then a naked lady pops into my head.

I blink again. I open my eyes and the headlights crawl down the hill at Main Street. The ground is cold; oak trees creak in the breeze. Strips of hard snow shine under the moon. The ravine is deep. The tiny streetlights change from green to yellow to red and I blink again and again. A white cloud floats out of the millstacks and reaches up the valley. I blink. Again. The devil whispers.

August, 2002. *I'm 38. The devil whispers again. I try to ignore him as I gently turn the wheel and watch the Mackinac Bridge slip past the edge of my rear view mirror. My wife turns in her seat to get one last look. "I don't think we got much of the bridge in the picture."*

"We got plenty of the bridge in the picture," I say, as I notice another heart palpitation. I blink.

"What's wrong?"

"Nothing," I say, as I feel another palpitation.

I've had my heart checked dozens of times over the course of nearly twenty years. My doctors have done EKGs and echocardiograms. There is nothing wrong with my heart.

Obsessive-compulsive disorder is my devil.

As a child, I only heard about the devil from the evangelists I saw on television. But I never heard about obsessive-compulsive disorder (OCD). Symptoms of OCD—intrusive thoughts and repetitive habits—have been part of my life for as long as I can remember.

Even now, as a 38-year-old writer, OCD exerts a powerful influence on me. As Liz and I return from a week-long writer's conference in Baltimore, my anxiety grows. I didn't get an offer from any agent or editor. My best essay didn't even place in the top three in the workshop. Perhaps, however, my efforts at the workshop will help me improve my portfolio enough to earn a scholarship to an MFA program at one of my chosen universities. Otherwise, having returned to college to earn a fine arts degree in creative and professional writing, I don't know how I'm going to find a job. My thoughts race like angry bees around a threatened hive. My tense muscles crave the narcotic of ritual. Anxiety approaches crescendo.

When I was in middle school, my anxiety approached a similar crescendo. I was shy and skinny—girls didn't talk to me. I was scrupulous and doubtful—God didn't seem to listen to me. But the devil rode comfortably upon my shoulder.

April, 1977. I blink when I pass the eighth-grade girls in the hall, the girls with tight sweaters and tighter blue jeans. My belt is notched too tight, just so I can keep my tails tucked deep so my underwear never shows. Every time I look at a girl too long I blink, and I whisper a prayer so fast that not even the devil can interrupt: "GodpleaseforgivemeforthesinIjustdidAmen."

Words are too slow for some of my prayers. Some of my prayers are just breaths: I breathe out sin and doubt. I breathe in faith and forgiveness.

Breathe out. Breathe in. I breathe out sin and doubt; I breathe in faith and forgiveness. I step with my left foot, then with my right. I watch my feet—left foot, right foot, bad foot, good foot, bad stair, good stair—as I walk across the landing, past the window, against the crowd. When I reach the top of the stairs, I go straight to the library. My left hand opens the door and my right hand helps it shut.

Labor Day, 2002. *Consolidated Freightways—the third largest trucking company in the United States—has been ordered to go under lockdown. A small detail of private security guards, we enter the Shoreview, Minnesota property just before dawn. Rod, my new boss, unlocks the padlock, then Jesse and I roll the gate open.*

We close the gate as a man on a forklift approaches us. Rod walks into the headlight beams, signals the driver to stop and hands him a slip of paper—the poor guy is instantly out of work. After a brief search, we conclude that the forklift driver is the only employee on-site. The angry truck-drivers and the news cameras won't arrive till tomorrow. For now, it is my job to guard a warehouse full of stranded cargo.

The sun rises. I take my post among a line of empty semi-trailers along the back fence. Soon, my uniform begins to dampen with sweat. After I eat my breakfast, I have nothing left to do. I find a patch of gravel behind one of the trailers and I begin to throw one rock at a time at a fencepost twenty paces away. The fencepost rings when I hit it. I begin to compete in an imaginary gravel-throwing tournament: I throw first, my opponent throws second.

The game helps me forget about my heart. I'm winning anyway; I win five rounds in a row. My uneven play, however, begins to make me uncomfortable: I don't aim as well when I throw for my opponent. My anxiety begins to mount. This imaginary gravel-throwing match is not only unfair—it violates my compulsion for symmetry.

Compulsive behaviors that occur in pairs are a fundamental symptom of OCD. In the spring of '77, left always compelled an answer from right. Walking, breathing, and blinking were subject to my secret count. What I did, I did twice. And if I passed through a door with my left foot or neglected to exhale a doubt, a bad feeling would linger until I corrected my "sin."

As an adult, I am still aware of my breaths, blinks, and footsteps—at some times more aware than at others. I'm most compulsive when I'm doing something boring—like guarding the fence behind a loading dock. When I was 13, a similar increase in my compulsive behaviors preceded a new and ominous obsession.

April, 1977. I count my steps as I walk across the library. Dust swims in the sun and icicles drip shadows across the rug. The sun lights my shoulders and makes my blood warm. The long, wooden drawers are all in the cabinet. Here it is: a drawer labeled "MA-MS." I flip the cards: "Mead, Meal, Meany, Meat...." Nothing. I walk over to the corner, fall to my knees, and look at the shiny letters on the backs of the encyclopedias. I pull out the big, fat volume labeled "M" and I flip the pages. There it is, right at the top of the page: MEASLES.

Brad is home with the measles: he is my lab partner in biology. Those are Brad's dirty fingers I remember as they dragged a razor blade across the belly of a dead frog. That is Brad's onion breath I smell while I remember him shouting, "Wow! Cool!" This is Monday; that was Friday. I count the hours between Monday and Friday while my eyes grab three terrible facts from the encyclopedia: measles are "ruddy" and "brown;" it takes three weeks to be sure you didn't catch them; and I need a booster shot.

I close the heavy book and place it back with the rest. The windows shine. Mud-splattered buses splash away along the puddled street. I cross the room and push the door open with both my hands.

I look at my hands, checking for spots. I check my forehead for a fever, and then I check it again. The staircase is empty. I walk across the landing, past the window, down the steps. Tucking my fists into the pockets of my windbreaker, I open the door with my shoulder—my left shoulder—and I nudge the door shut with my right.

October, 2002. *My temporary job is over. The Teamsters made a deal that permitted their drivers to ship the stranded cargo. The tension that erupted at the loading docks in Chicago and Pittsburgh failed to materialize in this suburb north of St. Paul.*

I'm obsessed with my heartbeat again. I wear a highly sensitive heart monitor beneath my heavy shirt. Liz sits beside me in the front of the pontoon boat as my father steers it across windy Lake Minnetonka. Only she knows what I'm wearing beneath my shirt.

"It sure is cold," says my mother.

"We'll be there in just a minute," says my father, pointing across the bay toward Maynard's lakeside restaurant, "and there are no other boats tied at Maynard's dock."

I casually run my fingers over the inner side of my wrist, searching for my pulse. As the rough water causes the boat to shudder, I cross my arms over my chest, protecting the monitor. I'll have to wait a couple weeks for the results.

In the spring of 1977, however, I couldn't just wait to find out if I had the measles. What if more kids were infected? Maybe an epidemic was coming? I just couldn't bear the thought of getting a booster shot. I figured out that three weeks is 504 hours. That was when ritual conquered logic and action replaced anxiety.

The connections between my rituals and fears were sometimes fairly obvious to me—like exhaling a breath and committing a sin. Other rituals, like blinking in response to intrusive thoughts, were connected a bit more subtly. During my seventh-grade measles scare, however, I fell victim to a ritual that took me twenty years to understand.

April, 1977. The sun is already down in the tree branches, and the lawn is full of cold puddles. The concrete is dry except for the streaks where the trees drop their shadows. I step over each of the cracks in the sidewalk, first with my left foot, then with my right, and I march between the ballfields and the gutter.

I stop beside the grate on the corner, where the cold water falls. Something sparkles on the sunny pavement. Glass. A tiny sliver of glass. My shadow gets thin when I stand and it follows me across the street. My shadow follows me back. I never thought of it before: glass in the street is dangerous.

I pick up another sliver of glass, and then another. In the mud beside the curb I find a bottlecap, rusted and sharp, and stuff it into my pocket. I find a pretty sharp stone near the middle of the street. Right in the middle of the street, right around the manhole cover, there is more glass, glittering in the sun.

My coat pockets are full, but the street is still covered with sharp, little things. But halfway home I stop: two beer bottles are bashed on a gravel driveway. Splinters of glass are everywhere.

Why clean it up? No one will walk across this filthy driveway with bare feet! If a car tire pops, a car tire pops—someone will just have to buy a new one. Then the devil whispers: "What if the tire doesn't pop? What if a tiny splinter of glass gets stuck in the rubber and digs a little bit deeper into the tread every time the tire rubs the street? What if that splinter of glass finally causes a blowout on the freeway?"

November, 2002. *I have the results: my heart is still fine. As usual, my doctor tells me there is nothing to worry about. My only worry is my new job.*

Rod found me a position at the rigidly-controlled, national headquarters of United Health Group in a ten-story building along a busy highway in Minneapolis. I work the second shift, checking every door, every stairwell, and every cubicle. It takes two hours to do my patrol—if I don't go back and double-check anything. But I always double-check.

"Did I check the freezer temperature?" I wonder, as I stop again to admire the Picasso outside the CEO's office on the tenth floor. "What if the food thaws just a little so that the cook doesn't notice but enough that everyone in the building gets food poisoning?" I ride the elevator

all the way back down to the maintenance rooms in the basement. I stop to re-read the Dilbert comic strips taped to the concrete walls, then I walk into the kitchen and see my initials on the sheet, entered 90 minutes earlier.

Obsessive-compulsive disorder offers a choice: obsess on a frightening thought or act by repeated compulsion. Think or do. Think, think, think or do, do, do. Do I want to take the elevator all the way back down to the basement, or do I want to worry about frozen food for the rest of my shift? Did I want to gather glass from a muddy driveway all day or lie awake all night thinking about tires exploding? Riding the elevator beat worrying, and gathering glass from a muddy driveway beat lying awake thinking about tires exploding. Anything beat lying awake wondering whether I had the measles.

April, 1977. The knees of my corduroys are wet from muddy gravel. My back and my shoulders are sore. My fingers are dirty and cold. An old man crosses the porch across the street, and then he goes inside. The woman next-door pulls her shade down. The shadows get longer and winter sneaks back.

There, near an old, beat-up car, another handful of glass. Almost enough for me to walk over and drop it in the dented trashcan across the driveway. The driveway is just about clean now. I've pretty much found every piece of the beer bottles.

Something grumbles—I barely hear it. The grumbling gets louder; it echoes in my ear. I turn my head—my nose almost rubs the cold, steel bumper of the car that has just pulled into the driveway. I straighten my legs until I can see over the rusty, brown hood. Two long-haired guys stare at me from behind the filthy windshield; their hairy faces turn angry behind the clean spots on the glass.

I run. I run as fast as I can, spilling glass as I dart between the houses. Tires splash in the puddles on the long-haired guys' driveway. A car door slams, and then the other one slams too. But I don't hear any footsteps. Three blocks away, I slow down. Glass jingles in my coat pocket.

I breathe hard, in and out. My breath is white. I stop and think.

This is Lake Street, a block from the little road up the hill. Wheeler Avenue—three whole blocks of it—might be covered with broken glass, rusted bottlecaps and pointy stones. And what about Monroe Avenue? What about Pierce or Van Buren? The worst and most deadly hazard—the one I might be meant to find—could be anywhere. It's already getting dark; my parents must be worried. Why in the heck am I so worried about car tires anyway?

March, 2003. *Liz and I stop for lunch at the Amana Colony on our way back from a visit to the University of Iowa. Though I lost my job at United Health Group in November, I won a place in the MFA program at Iowa. However, I didn't get a scholarship. We need to decide: Is it worth it? Should we take out another school loan? Should Liz quit the well-paying job she just found?*

"These are just like the curtains in the dream!" I say, reaching over a steaming bowl of mashed potatoes to point at the checkered, blue curtains beside our table. "And look at the pictures on the wall…They're black and white, just like in the dream. Maybe it's a sign."

"But no one is playing Bocce Ball, are they?" says Liz, trying not to sound exasperated as she points out the window at the tourists walking up and down the sunny sidewalk. "I don't think the Amish even approve of Bocce Ball. Everyone in your dream was playing Bocce Ball, right?"

My obsession with these coincidences is ridiculous—I know it myself. The similarities between a springtime Sunday in Iowa and the so-called "prophetic" dream I had five years earlier are purely coincidental. The similarities between my adolescent compulsion to collect sharp objects and my obsession with the measles, however, were not coincidental.

In the spring of '77, I didn't notice any similarity between a sharp object puncturing rubber and a hypodermic needle puncturing skin. I didn't notice any resemblance between a virus incubating in my body and a sliver of glass embedded in a car tire. My greatest fear was that I'd break out in measles right in the middle of class: a catastrophe as sudden and terrible to a 13-year-old boy as a blowout on the freeway.

April, 1977. Walking up the gravel road, by the first curve, I see the streetlights shining on the dangerous streets below me. Halfway up the road, by the clearing where a house used to be, the lengthening shadows swallow me. After the last curve, where I start the hardest part of my climb, day turns to night.

Headlights come toward me when I duck under the dead-end sign. A silver Toyota rolls to the end of the street and stops by the curb. I open the door and slump into the seat next to my father, my pockets stuffed with glass, a long, sharp stick in my hand. My father slowly shifts the car in gear and turns toward home.

"Where have you been?" he asks. "Your mother is worried sick."

"I picked up some broken glass on the street," I say, "and I cleaned up two broken bottles in a driveway."

"Why?"

"Because glass pops car tires."

While the dishes soak in the sink and my dirty clothes tumble in the wash, my father explains to me about car tires. "It's good that you're so concerned about other people," he says, "but do you really think a little piece of glass like the ones you had in your pockets can pop a car tire?"

I shrug my shoulders.

"Car tires are not just made of rubber; there's a steel belt under the tread. Protecting car tires from a pocketful of glass is like protecting a knight from a thumbtack."

My father is telling the truth, and I believe him. I go downstairs and turn the television on. There is no Oral Roberts tonight, no Rex Humbard, no evangelists at all—only Hawkeye, Radar, and Klinger. I sit in the brown rocker and my fingers play along the shapes carved into the wooden armrests. I rock, and I watch the streetlight through the high, little window. Then I close my eyes and whisper a prayer: "LordpleaseorgivemefornotfindingalltheglassAmen."

May, 2003. *It is only after many prayers that Liz and I decide against the MFA program at the University of Iowa. Instead, I take a job as a teacher at a one-to-one tutoring school in a suburb north of St. Paul. As a substitute, I teach a different subject every hour.*

My second-hour student arrives at the door of my tiny classroom pulling a wheeled suitcase full of secret possessions. He slumps into the chair across from me and pulls his baseball cap down over his eyes. His feet don't quite reach the floor. "I'm mad," he says, just as he had yesterday.

"It's okay to be mad, Chris," I say, slowly sliding his math book across the table, open to the page just past the last one he scribbled on. "You're not too mad for fractions, are you?" He scribbles out the equations on the fresh page.

"I'm really mad," he says.

We sit there in silence, staring across the table at one another. Up and down the hallways, teachers teach and students respond—I'm not good at this. I'm out of ideas. My heart skips a beat. I blink my eyes. My feet softly tap on the carpet: one-two, left-right, bad-good—

"Are those your cats?" asks Chris, suddenly pointing to a picture on the bookshelf behind me.

"Yes. The black one is Janey, and this is Otis," I say, pointing to the tabby.

"How old are they?"

I have to think for a minute. "Well, let's see… Janey is a year and nine months and Otis is a year and eight months." I think for a minute. "How old is that in people years?"

"In people years?"

"Yes. Isn't a cat year seven people years?" I ask.

"I think so."

I reach for a marker and walk to the little dry-erase board on the wall. I write:

$$Janey = 1\ 9/12 \qquad Otis = 1\ 8/12$$

"Now, in order to figure out how old they are in people years, we have to convert these mixed numbers to fractions."

I sit down and let Chris go to the board. He writes:

$$Janey = 21/12 \qquad Otis = 20/12$$

"Now, if a cat year is seven human years," I say, "we have to multiply our fractions by seven. Do you know how to do that?"

Chris writes it on the board. Then he writes his answers.

"Now, divide and convert the improper fractions back to mixed numbers," I say.

He writes: $Janey = 12\ 1/4 \qquad Otis = 11\ 2/3$

"They're both older than me!" shouts Chris.

"That's right. Now, can you figure how old they'll be when you're 13?"

May, 1977. Three weeks go by. No fever. No rash. No ruddy, brown spots. The booster shot hurt. But I don't have the measles.

When the bell rings, I follow the crowd across the landing, past the window, down the stairs. I climb on the bus and sit by the window. My neck is sore. The clouds race behind the treetops: big, puffy, friendly clouds. Cyclones don't drop from white, puffy clouds. White, puffy clouds don't make the sirens howl; white, puffy clouds don't make families run down into basements. But I keep looking up.

I step off the bus in front of my house and I stare at the sky, looking for dark clouds. Everyone on the bus watches me through the windows. As the bus rumbles away, I walk across the vacant lot to the trail between the trees. The path is wet from melting snow. Little buds sit on the tree branches. The sun cuts the edge of a cloud and spills into the woods. My little patch of dirt between the oak trees is dry. I breathe out. I breathe in. I stare at the sky, watching the clouds.... The devil is quiet today.

August, 2004. *Today, therapeutic drugs help me control my occasional spells of obsession with germs or heart palpitations. Daily activities, like running and swimming, make it difficult for me to compulsively count my breaths, blinks, and footsteps. Simply recognizing the connections between my irrational fears and my unnecessary habits—like the connection I finally noticed between dreading the measles and picking up glass—makes life a lot easier. However, I am humble enough to recognize that insight, exercise, and even medication cannot make me immune from the forces of anxiety. If I listen too closely, the devil still whispers. OCD is a formidable adversary: it doesn't matter whether my compulsion is gathering sharp objects from the ground or monitoring my heartbeat, whether my obsession is with catching the measles or finding a job.*

Teaching is my new obsession; it doesn't matter whether I teach fractions, psychology, or grammar. That is not to say that I never count heartbeats or blink before my eyes require it. The devil seems to whisper more softly, however, when I'm busy doing something I care about. Writing is something I care about. Helping my special-needs students express their struggles in words is a job I was born to do. When I'm not teaching students to write, I'm still writing myself.

Today, I've scribbled some notes for a new essay about a challenging and beautiful drive along California's Pacific Coast Highway. Having wound our way along the high, narrow curves from Monterey to San Francisco, Liz and I stand in the fog above the Golden Gate Bridge. She hands our camera to a friendly Englishman in a blue jacket. "How do you feel?" Liz asks me.

I smile as I put my arm around her.

The camera clicks. ❧

Before Spring

Alice Rose George

They promised snow, but, of course,
it is a pitiful rain—no two-footer
of paradise, white-covered all.

            Today, I found her
walking among the last camellias (because
it is spring there, and they are making room for
spirea, red bud, and azalea).
I saw sunlight play on her silver hair,
on her eyes nearly blind—and all the rest
of pain living under her skin. But, today,
I found her walking in the sun, touching camellias.

I want to hold the door for her coming in
to answer the phone and in talking to see the mother
she always was and is again—at least today. Today when
the snow storm skipped us and I walked in plain
rain and wished to be snow-covered, a fallen
angel—also, a camellia before spring.

        ꙮ

Before It's Begun

Alice Rose George

It happened in fall,
now it happens in spring:
I smell summer in winter's coming,
the autumn chorus of crickets
creeps between the shades of lilac.
The world revolves too fast,
we are approaching the age of frenzy,
my foot can't slow this
racing machine as it did
my bike as a child. But, gone too,
are the afternoons spent dreaming
of a life to come, of the shape
love might take. Now, it is done
before it is begun, and the faces
that carry these lives—ours—
turn to stone as they slip on
the most important experiences.
Considering, one would think
death existed before life ended
but death, at least, holds itself noble
—unless you consider depression—
above the fray, no rush coming.
Maybe I am yesteryear's person.

     I turn to walk through the gardens.
Birds portend next year's crop,
but they comfort me just the same.
Vague words of compromise hang
here and there in the wisteria.
I will grow tulips in snow
and hope for iced sheets in August.

   80

Stories from the Other Side of Silence

Patricia O'Hara

"No story is the same to us after a lapse of time," wrote George Eliot, and then qualified the statement by adding, "or rather we who read it are no longer the same interpreters." When I read *Peter Pan and Wendy* as a girl, I envied the freedom of the Lost Boys; when I read it as a woman, I grieved for their orphaned state.

Stories change, but there's one story I return to again and again.

It's my mother's story I'm referring to, a particular chapter of it when I was a teenager. If it were just her story, perhaps I could settle on a version of it, accept that it was a narrative construction, and be done with it. But it's also my story and so, a couple years ago, I requested the medical records from the psychiatric hospital where, from 1968 to 1970, my mother was institutionalized.

She was admitted on three occasions during those years for periods of time from three to eight weeks, for suicide attempts, alcoholism, and depression. Those mental breakdowns were not without precedent in her life. Eight years earlier she'd spent time in a facility in Westport, Connecticut, and in her thirties there was a drying-out place or two elsewhere. But the breakdowns at the end of the 1960's—those were something else entirely. Or so it seemed to me then. And so it seems to me even now, when I think about that lonely time in which the central fact of my adolescent existence was that I harbored a shameful, unspeakable secret and needed to invent lies to account for my mother's absence, even though the people who listened to my tales probably knew some or all of the facts.

After 1970—the year I graduated high school—my mother was never institutionalized again. She recovered from her alcoholism and managed to lead, by most people's standards, a more or less functional life, one punctuated by spells of something like contentment. To be sure, she remained, in the words of the institution's 1970 discharge report, "a very immature individual with intense dependency needs which show[ed] themselves directly through her demands on people and indirectly through physical symptoms." But she held down various jobs, was active in AA, and socialized with a small but close circle of women friends. I went to college for a while, moved to a Caribbean island, banged around for a few years, and eventually found my way into what is, by most people's standards, a highly functional life as a professor of literature at a liberal arts college. After 1970, I never lived at home again.

And after 1970, no one in my family of three ever talked about those hospitalizations. Or maybe my parents talked to each other about them, but they never talked to me. An occasional remark might slip loose from its moorings, but nothing ever hit the mark. There was no moment in a dialogue when I hazarded, "how did things get so bad for you?" or when she offered, "I was in tough shape back then."

Sometimes it seems as if it never happened, or as though it happened in someone else's family, or to some girl who went to a different high school, or who was the cousin of a friend of a friend. The strange otherness of the experience has served me well at the times when it was useful—even essential— to misplace my family history and reinvent myself: as twenty-something drifter, as somebody's girlfriend, somebody's graduate student, somebody's professor. The alterity of the past has been my source of strength. But it has served me less well at other times. No matter how many ways you reinvent yourself, you can't keep that sort of history at arm's length indefinitely, unnarrated and unattended. It takes its toll.

So I've been hunting down the past in the aging medical records with their pages of psychoanalytic and medical data that contain the most painful stories of our lives, hers and mine. Reading the records helps me to assemble the puzzles of my particular life in my particular family. And I'm sustained by a belief that these stories matter, not just for their disclosures about my particular self, but for their intersection with strands of the larger web of human experience that becomes evident through the stories we tell and the stories we hear. True memoir, Patricia Hampl reminds us, is written in an attempt to find not only a self but a world.

It was probably a couple of old letters written on pale blue stationery that prompted me to make the phone call to the medical records office of the hospital where my mother spent 122 days suffering from what was diagnosed as schizophrenia, schizo-affective disorder, hypertension, and alcoholism. Not long ago, I came upon the letters and willed myself to read them, and then read them again. I don't think I'd read them through in years, maybe never, since they were originally sent in 1968. When I'd previously happened upon them at odd moments, I would start reading but the words would deliver too hard a blow to the center of my chest. Too painful to remember, I'd tell myself, and stick them back in the bag. Now, years later, however, I felt with conviction that it was time to read them, that I'd reached a point in my life when I was required to read them.

March 3, 1968
Dear Pat,

It seems kind of funny to be writing you a letter but here goes. I meant to write sooner but just received this paper. I can say one thing about this place, it sure is cold....Pat please write to me as I get so lonely for you....please believe I will soon be well & home & things will be very different....Please take good care of yourself as I love you very much and I'm so proud of you in everything you do. Please excuse this writing. This is the worst pen I have ever used.

All My Love, Mom xxx

P.S. Please write to me soon

This is the first of two letters from my mother early in her hospitalizations. There may have been more. I kept these two letters in a plastic bag that holds the sum of my high school mementos: notes passed to me during class, cards from friends, tickets from school plays, a graduation program. I am surprised that I didn't lose the bag over the years, having moved around so much. I have no recollection of deliberately holding on to those two letters or the scraps of high school memories, but their survival testifies to the agency of the unconscious. I must have known, in some fashion or another, that someday I was going to need those letters.

From this vantage point, after a lapse of decades, I experience that first letter as shot through with pathos, punctuated with all those pleases, and written by a person suspended in a place where access to pens and paper was restricted. I imagine myself in my high school uniform reading the letter in 1968, sitting alone in the living room of a small house on High Street in a small town in southern New England. My father worked two jobs: days in a ball-bearing factory and nights in a restaurant. After school, before going to my Aunt Mary's house where I would spend most nights, I would come home, change, and go to work at my part-time job in a home fuel oil company.

I imagine myself reading the letter, then tensing my jaw to tamp down the sadness that would rise, unbidden. And then I'd shake it off, have a cigarette and a Coke, and leave the house for work, perhaps repeating to myself the words of consolation about her institutionalization, words that I'd heard over and over from my father and my aunt: It's for the best. It really is for the best, you know.

For the best for whom? I used to think.

March 12, 1968
My Dear Pat,

Hi love. Just received your sweet card. It only took one day to get here. I was surprised to hear you felt well enough to work so soon. Please try & do not overdo it. Nothing new here. Same old thing. But Pat it really is a very good hospital & believe it or not I do like the Dr. I just find it hard at times to talk to him. I'm making a hot plate in O.T. ha ha! I'll give the baskets a rest….tell everyone to write to me. Pat give the meat in the freezer to Mary. Be good and take care because I love you very much.

Love, Mom

P.S. Water plant & change sheets often. Have Dad sweep sidewalks often.

One thing I know for sure about my mother's experience in that hospital: she hated Occupational Therapy. I remember her making fun of herself and what she perceived as her ineptitude at arts and crafts projects. I assume that a patient's cooperation in Occupational Therapy was one measure by which the mental health care professionals gauged their patients' recovery. This letter shows either that my mother knew how to please or that the staff effectively enforced participation in OT. She completed the hot plate, made of small, black and white mosaic tiles glued onto a fiberboard backing and then grouted. It was like something you'd make from a kit bought at a hobby shop: simple, functional, generic. When I was in my twenties, she gave it to me for some apartment or other, and I carried it around for years until it started falling apart. Another person would have gotten rid of that hot plate sooner, and I've sometimes worried about my inclination to hold on to bits and pieces from my mother's past—wondered if it's symptomatic of an inability to move on, or to let go of sadness. Yet, rereading the letter suggests that there's never just one way of interpreting our own actions: perhaps somewhere in the deep recesses of memory, I associated the hot plate with a loving letter from my caring but troubled mother to me, the daughter she had to leave at home while she tried to get better at the hospital.

Still, the letter opens up multiple possibilities. My mother's remembering the meat in the freezer and the houseplant in the living room might seem a reassuring sign that ordinary domestic life still beckoned. That she missed her home and putting the roast in the oven right after ten o'clock Mass. That she missed me. Yet her mental illness had burdened me with watching over her and her safety and trying to prop up a wobbly household while going to school, holding a job, and doing homework. Read from the perspective of *my* experience, her reminding me of the chores I had to perform was just one more manifestation of her "demands on people." At once solicitous and demanding, thoughtful and self-absorbed, the letter evokes the emotional push and pull that changed only by degree, not kind, in the after-years of those crisis times.

For most of my adult life I have brushed off, with discomfort, friends' admiration for my "resilience" in the face of such challenges. That way lies self-pity, and I fear self-pity as a dangerous trap: quicksand. My way has been to say that I did what I had to do to get through and get out, and that resilience isn't a sign of strength, just an instinct for survival. But when I read the letters and the medical records and the narratives they encrypt, I've come to acknowledge that it must have been very hard for that lonely teenaged girl, and that getting out was no small accomplishment, after all.

On a warmish day in October 2001, a year after my father sold the house on High Street and moved into a retirement community, a couple of months into a sabbatical designated for writing a book on Victorian farm workers, and a short while after I'd read my mother's letters to me from the hospital, I decided to call that institution to request her records. I have tried to reconstruct what chain of reasoning led me to pick up the phone to call directory assistance that day, but I can't trace it out with any certainty.

Maybe autumn conjured up yearnings for a past before my mother's sickness, for walking up High Street after school, stopping to pick up fallen chestnuts in a neighbor's front yard, peeling back the spiny seed pods, and stuffing the glossy nuts in my book sack. Or maybe I was just beginning to feel restless and bored with literary scholarship: I had occupied myself for so many years with other people's stories that it was time to start penciling in the margins of my own.

What arrived just before Christmas was a thick white envelope, the kind with visible fibers, like wisps of white hair, enmeshed in the paper. You could never accidentally tear open an envelope like that. It's the sort to which you have to take a pair of scissors and cut a crosswise gash to get at the contents inside.

The records that I removed from the envelope were both more and less than I expected. They comprised 212 pages, fastened into three packets, one for each hospital stay: 2-28-68 through 4-17-68; 1-16-69 through 2-4-69; and the final stay from 11-23-69 to 1-20-70. Each packet contained medication charts, test results, psychiatrists' reports (admission and discharge summaries as well as progress notes) along with observation logs filled in by the morning, evening, and night shift staff.

In all of the documents I am mentioned just a handful of times and identified only as "the patient's daughter." In some ways, my absence in the pages comes as a relief; I can feel sure now that I wasn't the cause of her problems—the irrational fear of every child of the mentally ill. In other ways, it's a disappointment to me that maybe I didn't count for all that much.

Yet my past is indelibly written into those records in the staggering number of references that rise up like so many specters out of the staff reports, even in easily-overlooked stray pages. My father's signature in a visitor's log, for instance, indicates that on December 7, 1969, he visited my mother in the hospital but that I did not accompany him. It was a Monday, thus one of the two nights my father had off from the restaurant. I had visited her only a few times, and I certainly would not have gone on a school night. Even though I don't remember that particular occasion, I'm certain it must have registered with me at the time.

December 7, 1969 was my seventeenth birthday.

Where was I on my seventeenth birthday? Staying with my aunt? Did we celebrate my birthday, maybe with a Carvel ice cream cake that I would have shared with her two younger sons? Did I talk to my mother on the phone?

The night before my birthday, my mother had, according to the records, "apparently slept well" but that day she was "very loud at times. Also appears very angry & sarcastic when talking about family." Sometime before 11 PM on my seventeenth birthday she "visited with husband" and afterward "display[ed] sarcastic humor" when back on the floor.

Where was I?

And who were all those people writing the psychiatric documents? As I read these records, dozens of narrators speak to me: psychiatrists, attendants who wrote in the daily logs, and RNs who initialed the meds charts. Theirs was a professional relationship with my mother. Some observed her actions; others wrote diagnoses. The logs tell me stories in clipped phrases and handwriting that becomes familiar after a while. There's the one log-writer who used the word "sarcastic" all the time, and the one who thought it important to note when my mother was "neatly groomed." The one whose penmanship was rarely readable. And the one who sounded disappointed when my mother started acting out and lost her phone privileges and off-grounds privileges.

There's the morning attendant who observed with approval one day that my mother was tidy and dressed in a "young modern style." And there's the afternoon attendant who noted later that same day that my mother was dressed "immaturely for her actual age." She was 38 years old.

So many narrators contend for my attention with their descriptions of my mother that it's hard to assemble a coherent narrative of the past. And yet a story of her illness gets mapped across the notes that record a linear sequence, shift by shift, day by day. And the plot that emerges across the three bundles of documents reveals her illness escalating and deepening, from her first stay in 1968 to her final release in 1970. Her disintegration appears particularly acute during the approach of Christmas 1969. My mother was upset that she had not been granted an overnight pass to spend Christmas night at home, though she would be able to visit us on Christmas Day. Even though I feared her behavior and my father's angry reprisals (often fueled by his own alcoholism), I, too, was probably disappointed that she could not spend Christmas night at home with us. On December 22, the 3-11 shift attendant recorded that: "Pt appeared to upset easily this evening—ran into her room crying & yelling one time this evening. It appears that she is anxious about how her daughter is enjoying Christmas this year."

My mother had always liked Christmas and decorating the house with knick-knacks and a tree. She liked getting and giving gifts and arranging glossy ribbon candy in dishes. I did all the wrapping of gifts that weren't for me because I enjoyed it—curling ribbons with the sharp edge of the scissors, making gift cards with sequins and glue, measuring the paper so that the folded flaps would come out even—and because my mother, we both agreed, had little patience or aptitude for the task. I think I remember—I can't be sure after so many years—trying to decorate the house that year in her absence. I think I remember sullenly putting up a Christmas tree and going through the motions of trimming it. I don't remember about the gifts.

By that Christmas Eve my mother was scared about the impending home-visit the next day. The attendant described her as "fearful of what will happen on visit home on Christmas Day. Knows that she must not partake of alcohol but feels that she must have maybe two drinks." This was not a good omen. Not at all. When my mother had day passes, my father would take her out and order drinks; that's one reason I rarely accompanied him on those visits.

How strange then that I can recall nothing of that Christmas spent with my mother out on her day pass. Did we eat at a restaurant? Or at my Aunt Mary's? (I dismiss the latter as doubtful, given that my mother was always made "nervous" by the noise and confusion of my aunt's household.) I've tried to remember, to call up any image that might bring some of it back. But nothing rises to the surface.

Strange, this forgetfulness, but not surprising when I read the account of her condition later that night, back at the hospital. By 11 PM of Christmas night she was walking down the hall, carrying a doll and saying, "This is my daughter Eileen." She was given meds and returned to her room, but re-emerged at 5 AM,

… stumbling down hall. In an attempt to take her back to bed, pt found to have safety pin in rt hand and scratching her left fore-arm longitudinally (not bleeding). Pt resisted when pin was taken away from her & started biting and scratching (with nails) herself. Pt said she felt she had wronged the staff and therefore punishing herself. Reasoning failed to calm her so she had to be held down forcibly. Even after medications pt was still trying to harm herself so body restraints used and pt placed on 1:1 & secluded.

She was given 50 milligrams of Thorazine. The 6 -7AM entry notes that the patient was sleeping and the restraints were removed.

It's not surprising then that I can't remember the day that ended with my mother having a psychotic episode. Who would wish to preserve such memories? And who would wish to retrieve the details of what could only have been a nightmare holiday? It's enough for me to settle for a tiny insight into the difficult time I often have at Christmas. Why I try to compensate by baking platters of cookies for neighbors I barely know. Or why winter sometimes blindsides me with a hollowness that leaves me sleepless at night and exhausted during the day.

Yet even as I confront and admit how difficult a patient my mother must have been, I find myself resisting many of the records' representations of my mother's inner life. Often those psychiatrists' reports on my mother's condition sound strangely, infuriatingly dated. They read like caricatures of psychoanalytic practice. I could imagine seeing them in a novel, or a feminist critique of the treatment of women's mental illness in the 1960's: a *Yellow Wallpaper* for the Age of Aquarius. The psychiatric reports are full of phrases like "early oral fixation" and "pseudoneurotic pseudopsychopathic superstructure imposed upon underlying schizophrenia and paranoia" and "a nexus of massive distortion projections." They refer to Bender and Figure Drawing tests and Rorschach examinations.

When I come upon the following passage, for example, my resentment is visceral:

> Mental status shortly after admission showed a distraught, hostile woman who was fairly well groomed….At times, the patient was initially agreeable and compliant, but at times she became demanding. In several instances, she became intensely hostile towards the therapist. Repeatedly, she misinterpreted,

distorted, or used out of context ideas verbalized by the therapist, and it was felt that the primitive mechanisms of distortion, projection, and denial were much in evidence... During this admission, it seemed quite obvious that this patient is suffering from a schizophrenic illness which is felt to best be described as Schizo-affective in type. Although many paranoid elements were recognized.

I understand that this psychiatrist was merely writing in the professional discourse of his period, doing what he was trained to do. And I admit my subjectivity skews my response; this was the psychiatrist I met and did not like, the one my mother did not like either. However, I am a professionally-trained reader, and I do not trust this man's construction. I doubt he sought to treat my mother by listening to her, but rather by pouring her behaviors into diagnostic paradigms. He sought compliance and got hostility, so he blamed the patient for misinterpreting the ideas he verbalized and chalked it up to primitive mechanisms of distortion. He is not a reliable narrator. I do not trust him.

Not all the voices of professional authority are suspect, however. A few earn my confidence. There is, for instance, the psychologist who spun the inkblot test results into a diagnosis that respects the patient's experience and her humanity, while remaining clinical and professional in its verbal demeanor:

The poor prognostic picture of this patient is further established by the results of her Rorschach examination. What is suggested is that she has a poor self-concept. She sees herself as completely trapped and unable to spell out any goals for herself. She has tried to extricate herself but with no success, and, although preoccupied with her failures, she sees no resolution to her conflicts....Further testing into the Rorschach representations revealed a person who views reality as totally fragmented and disorganized...She is a woman who has felt rejected, unloved, and bears resentment toward all the circumstances that have continually deprived her of happiness: a bad childhood, a bad marriage, and bad acting out behavior. By stamping a value quality upon things she is able to punish herself further.

This man did not need inkblots shaped like asymmetrical butterflies to understand my mother's bad childhood and marriage. Maybe he thought he did; maybe he was obliged to affirm the tools of his trade in his formal reports.

What he needed—and amply possessed, I believe—was an ear tuned to the subtexts and a heart not closed to compassion.

It's easy to lose my way in these records, these papers that a writer friend calls my "great material." There are so many narrators, so many stories, so many mothers. Some days my postmodern sangfroid about indeterminacy rubs up against a vestigial longing for a singular True Story. I wish there were a single narrative I could extract from the gray and white leaves of the past. But there is not, and the best I can do is locate the bits of stories that possess the authority of felt truth, and move forward from there. It's the only way to live with the pieces that slip and slide and refuse to fall into place, pieces like the final pages of the records.

The last two entries in the staff logs written on the day my mother was discharged from her final stay at the hospital read: "Pt appears in good spirits. Prepared for discharge most of day. Socialized with other pts and staff in day room. Appetite good," and "Pt discharge[d] to husband. Appeared cheerful on approach." She must have been excited. And despite all the harrowing experiences I'd been through with her—the suicide attempts, the scenes in front of my friends and neighbors, her drunken nighttime rages and morning-after guilty regrets—I must have been excited too. I could go home. I could sleep in my own bed and not in the back-of-the-house drafty addition at my aunt's house. I could set up my easel and try oil painting again. It must have been hopeful, picking her up, putting her suitcases in the car, and driving back to the home I had vacuumed and dusted and stocked with groceries.

However, in the report written a week after her discharge, the psychiatrist overseeing my mother's treatment is far from sanguine in his prognosis for her future:

> It has been recommended to the family and to the patient that she be in the hospital for a number of months. It was felt that this would present the best chance for her....however it turned out that insurance coverage would not allow for this form of treatment...[S]he is felt to be a very immature individual with intense dependency needs which show themselves directly through her demands on people and indirectly through physical symptoms....[I]t is recognized that the outlook is quite poor and the patient's husband, sister, and daughter were informed of this.

The first time I read that I'd been informed of her state upon discharge, I was stunned, not so much that the future was not hopeful but that I had been included in the disclosure. I don't remember if my mother's doctor told me in person of her poor outlook or if it came to me second-hand. But something tells me—some physical sensation I experience in my stomach when I read that passage from the report—that I was informed directly by her psychiatrist of the poor prognosis. It must have been discouraging. It must have been hard to hold competing stories in my heart as we made the hour's drive back to the house on High Street.

My mother's stories are like those of Mrs. Darling described at the opening of *Peter Pan and Wendy*, as a woman with a "mind like the tiny boxes, one within the other, that come from the puzzling East, however many you discover there is always one more." These days, I think that the central emotional experience articulated in J. M. Barrie's children's story is the experience of absence. It's just that most of us don't remember that part. We remember the Lost Boys running rampant in fields of Neverland. We forget the lost mothers. And for a long time, too long a time perhaps, I had forgotten that, once upon a time, there was a lost daughter, too.

It's never easy going, reading my mother's records, traveling to the other side of silence. It was Eliot again who observed that "If we had a keen vision and feeling of all ordinary human life, it would be like hearing the grass grow and the squirrel's heart beat, and we should die of that roar which lies on the other side of silence." Some days, sitting in my sun-drenched study and listening to voices speaking from the hushed, cold past, I am troubled by the possibility that the journey's end might be a place where I know and see and hear too much. ❧

To My Mother, Dead Eight Years

Susan Rich

When I travel out of country
you can't follow as easily; can't click
your tongue around my thighs'
circumference, can't chart my unsocial
social life. I've flown Cape Town
to Jerusalem fleeing condemnation
yet, our cold words cling like the dying
roots of old pot-bound plants: cracked, unforgiven.

But that's just half the days, half
the lines inside my head. I've kept
the way you welcomed each guest:
candles lit at dusk on Friday evenings,
sweet fruit and chilled ginger ale. *Never
hate anyone* you said, but couldn't hold to.
And if there was little love to spare
we had crisp sheets, clean underwear.

&

In the Eye of History

Joseph Carlton Porter

I was twelve when my mother told me this story, but I have never repeated it to anyone, I suppose out of embarrassment, or doubt that it would even be believed, but the story has stayed with me like a proud family secret, and I have remained in awe of how my mother, in her compassion, affected world history.

My mother had grown up on a small farm in Westmoreland, New York, graduated from St. Elizabeth's School of Nursing in Utica and, because she was an excellent nurse, met some famous people in the course of her career.

As a private duty nurse in Los Angeles back in the 1930's, my mother took care of Mary Pickford in her home and got to know Douglas Fairbanks, Jr. Later, when Bing Crosby's wife, Dixie, came down with a kidney infection, my mother nursed her in their Toluca Lake mansion in North Hollywood and became friends with the singer. Early in her career, she took care of the hypochondriac, Mrs. Elihu Root, wife of the Nobel laureate and former Secretary of State.

After the Japanese bombed Pearl Harbor, it was my mother's intention to join the WAF, the Women's Air Force, but then something unexpected happened: having treated gunshot G-men at St. Elizabeth's, she was recommended for the FBI. When she took the train to Washington, D.C., she was surprised to be interviewed and hired by J. Edgar Hoover himself. It didn't hurt, I guess, that she was Catholic and her last name was Malone.

I was doing my homework for my 7th grade history class one night when my mother came into my room and sat on my bed. I was trying to decide which world leader I would write a book report on.

"You should write about de Gaulle," my mother said.

Charles de Gaulle? I was thinking more about Eisenhower or Churchill, though I had read how de Gaulle had organized the Free French Forces and supplied information to the French Resistance. What caught my imagination, though, was the fact that there had been a price on his head. Hitler and the Vichy government were trying to assassinate him.

"I could tell you something about him," she said.

"Like what, Mom?"

"I met him once."

"You're kidding, Mom? You met General Charles de Gaulle?"

She smiled ever so slightly.

"When? Where? Did you talk to him?"

"Oh, yes. We talked, though I must say it wasn't under the best of circumstances for either one of us."

"What do you mean—not under the best of circumstances? What happened? What was he like?"

She looked toward the window and was silent for what seemed like the longest time. Finally, she said, "Well, he was gallant. Yes, that's the word. He was very gallant."

"You mean he was a snob?" I asked.

"Oh, no. I mean he was courteous, very proper."

"What was he doing in America?"

"Well, I don't know, but I'm sure it was about the war."

"I bet he was there to talk to Harry Truman about the German surrender," I said. "V-E day!"

My mother smiled at my enthusiasm. She seemed to drift back in time, but apparently it wasn't de Gaulle's visit that made her remember that day so vividly.

It was Friday, June 8, 1945. My mother was finishing paperwork in her office at the National Airport, and thankfully, it wasn't busy that afternoon. She was supposed to get off work at three, and as the hour neared, she kept looking at the clock.

She had been anxious all day because that evening was her wedding rehearsal; and at dinner afterwards, she would be meeting her future mother-in-law for the first time, along with other relatives on my father's side. And the next day she was marrying my father, an Army Air Force captain, in the Walter Reed hospital chapel.

However, her most pressing concern was not the rehearsal or the meeting with my grandmother, but her wedding dress. She had to be at a bridal shop on Wisconsin Avenue by four to have her final fitting and pick up the dress before the shop closed at five. It wouldn't have been so troubling except that she had to catch the airport bus and then transfer to another bus to reach the bridal shop, all of which meant she had to leave work that day on time.

Despite this, it wasn't unusual for my mother to work until five or six o'clock if there were emergencies. And to make matters a little more complicated, Marge Fleming, the nurse who relieved my mother, tended to be five or ten minutes late every day, though she had promised my mother she would be on time that day.

As 3:00 P.M. neared, my mother grew more anxious. What if there was an emergency? What if Marge didn't make it on time and the bridal shop closed before she got there? What would she do? The shop wasn't open on Saturday.

She preferred not to think about any of those possible catastrophes, so she kept her mind on her work, but while she worked, she said a prayer.

When she finished the last of the paperwork, it was 2:30, and she gathered her cape and handbag so she would be all ready to leave as soon as Marge arrived. Again she glanced at the wall clock.

It wasn't unusual for my mother to see diplomats and heads of state pass through the airport, but when General Charles de Gaulle and a small entourage—the airport's director, the French ambassador, two American Secret Service agents, along with the General's bodyguard—stepped into her office, she was taken aback. Taken aback, not by the presence of this great man—whom she recognized immediately—but by the time: it was 2:40.

The airport's director introduced my mother as the Charge Nurse and a member of the FBI, and assured de Gaulle that Miss Malone, "a most capable nurse," could certainly handle his problem, thereby avoiding a needless trip to the hospital.

De Gaulle, though not handsome in the conventional sense, was quite tall and distinguished looking in his uniform and had the presence of a great stage actor.

At the moment though, my mother was so worried about her wedding dress that his presence didn't faze her. In fact, her only thought was: I hope this doesn't take long.

Being just 5 feet, 6 inches, my mother had to look up to the General, who was holding his right eye closed in obvious discomfort. Apparently, after exiting his plane, as he walked across the tarmac, whether it was prop blast or a gust of wind, a particle of grit had blown into the General's eye, and he'd felt a sharp sting. Neither blinking nor rubbing his eye could dislodge it.

When my mother showed the General into an examination room, his frowning bodyguard insisted on accompanying them. Though this was unusual and my mother didn't like it, there wasn't time to argue with the suspicious man.

My mother asked the General to sit down on the examination table while she quickly washed her hands in the porcelain sink. Normally she would have checked his vital signs—taken his pulse and temperature—but looking at her wristwatch she saw it was 2:45 and, considering the pain he was in, she skipped those procedures.

De Gaulle had a prominent nose, and under it, a neatly trimmed mustache. Two gold stars decorated his sleeve cuff. Leaning close, she smelled his aloe cologne. The bloodshot eye was slightly inflamed and tearing, and at first look, she didn't see the particle, yet holding his eyelids open, and having him roll his eye, she did see the speck—a tiny grit of sand—under the bottom eyelid.

"Oh, good. There it is, General. I'll have it out in a jiffy."

She immediately fashioned a saline-dipped cotton swab, and holding his eyelids open, reached in to remove the tiny irritant. But the General pulled back and she lost it.

"You just have to remain still, General. I won't hurt you."

She tried again to remove it, but when the tip of the swab skimmed the surface of the General's eyeball, once more he tensed and blinked, and she had to begin over.

My mother glanced at the bodyguard, who'd been watching every move she made. She checked her wristwatch. It was now 2:50—and where was Marge?

A third time she tried to remove it and almost had it. But once more the General flinched, and the foreign particle wouldn't adhere to the cotton swab. Her wristwatch now said 2:55. Oh, my God. She had just fifteen minutes to catch the bus. What was she going to do?

My mother put down the cotton swab. She wasn't one for losing her patience, but this wasn't working. Once more she looked toward the bodyguard whose presence had become a source of annoyance. "I'm sorry, General, but he's making me nervous."

De Gaulle said something in French. The bodyguard protested, but de Gaulle met it with a growl and the flick of his hand. The bodyguard reluctantly exited.

Now my mother knew another way to remove the particle, though you won't find this technique in any nursing textbook.

"General, I need you to keep your left eye shut."

"*Oui*," he said and obediently closed his left eye.

"And when I peel back your eyelid, I'll need you to look up at the ceiling light. Do you understand?"

"*Oui, Mademoiselle.*"

Sitting in my room, I stopped my mother in the middle of her story. "Holy cow! Mom, you didn't?"

Modestly, she nodded.

"Mom, no! Tell me you didn't do *that* to General Charles de Gaulle."

"Michael, I couldn't be late, and it was my duty as a nurse to relieve his discomfort."

"But Mom! Did he get mad?"

"No, of course not. He was appreciative."

"He was?"

When the particle of sand was out of De Gaulle's eye, my mother stepped back.

"*Ah, Mademoiselle! Trés bon.*" He immediately rose. "*Merci! Merci beaucoup.*"

The entourage in the waiting room stood up when my mother and de Gaulle walked out of the examination room. Everyone was relieved and smiling to see the General recovered and able to continue on with world affairs.

I was convinced that my mother's quick thinking had prevented infection and possibly blindness, and with his vision restored, de Gaulle was off to the White House and the Halls of Congress to win support for the rebuilding of France and the recovery of Europe.

A minute later Marge Fleming burst in out of breath. "Oh, Jane, I just saw—"

My mother already had her cape over her arm and bag in hand. "I know. I'll see you in the morning."

"Oh, yes. Yes, your wedding! I'm sorry I'm late, but—"

Without another word, my mother rushed out. She ran the whole way to catch the bus, and luckily, boarded it just before it pulled away. And as it happened, everything worked out well from there on: she transferred to the next bus, made it to the bridal shop on time, and her wedding dress fit perfectly. The following morning—"the happiest day in my life"—my mother married my father. After the reception, they took a train to New York City for their honeymoon.

A week later when, my mother returned to her job at the National Airport, flowers and a thank-you card from General de Gaulle were waiting for her. For three years, General de Gaulle sent her a Christmas card.

You see, I knew very well how my mother had removed the particle from the General's eye. When I was ten, while playing baseball one day in the park, the wind whipped a fiery cloud of dust into my face. I felt something sharp in my eye, and when it wouldn't come out, I had to dash home.

I ran into our house, holding my hand over my eye, tearing from the pain. My mother said, "Take your hand away, dear. Let me see."

Gently holding my eyelids open with her thumbs, she instructed me to look up at the ceiling. Then, as I focused on the kitchen globe, she swooped down on my eye. Like a French kiss, her tongue darted into the corner of my eye, where it lodged for the briefest second. Then gently, lovingly, it swept over the eyeball, sliding the offending sliver out from under the lid. And as soon as the sliver was out, the sting was gone.

"Mom, you got it!"

"Yes, darling." She smiled, pinching the tiny sliver of wood off the tip of her tongue.

Inspired by my mother's story, I wrote my book report on Charles de Gaulle, believing I shared a personal experience with the General, which gave me a unique perspective on that great man.

I did not put in the paper that my mother had met him, but I wrote about de Gaulle's bravery and how important he was to the French people during and after World War II. Sister Thomas Marie gave me a 97 (taking three points off for misspelling the word gallant).

President de Gaulle died in 1970, and my mother passed away in 1980. While I didn't think that my mother actually changed the course of world history, I knew that her act of compassion allowed General de Gaulle to continue on his mission and showed him—once more—that the Americans were his friends and that we could be counted on, and that there wasn't anything we wouldn't do to help him liberate his beloved country. ๕

Contributors' Notes

Colleen Abel has studied writing in America and England, and has an MFA from the Program for Writers at Warren Wilson College. She recently moved to the Chicago area from Astoria, Queens with her husband and hairless cat.

Amanda Auchter is the editor of *Pebble Lake Review* and recipient of the Howard Moss Poetry Prize. She was a finalist in the *Atlanta Review* International Poetry Competition and won third prize from *Writer's Digest* for creative nonfiction. Her writing has appeared or is forthcoming in *Born Magazine, Cimarron Review*, *DIAGRAM, Phoebe*, and *Sulphur River Literary Review*.

Alice Ayers' fiction has appeared in various literary journals, including *Other Voices* and *The Literary Review*, and has been nominated for a Pushcart Prize. Raised in South Carolina and a true Southerner at heart, she currently lives in Phoenix with her husband and two daughters. She teaches creative writing at Arizona State University.

Craig Boyer's essays have appeared in *Nostalgically, Blueline,* and *How Running Changed My Life*. He was also a finalist in *The New Millennium Writing Awards*. He teaches writing and philosophy at Calvin Institute, a private school and psychological clinic. He is currently writing a book that combines his training in philosophy with his experiences with obsessive-compulsive disorder. Craig and his wife Elizabeth live in St. Paul, Minnesota and expect their first child this spring.

William Bradley is a graduate student at the University of Missouri-Columbia, where he is studying the history of the personal essay and writing a memoir. His work has appeared in *The Missouri Review,* and he is the former nonfiction editor of *Center: A Journal of the Literary Arts*. His cancer has been in remission for almost five years; he hasn't watched *General Hospital* in nearly five months.

Seth Carey lives in the same house in West Falmouth, Cape Cod in which he grew up. ALS has taken away his ability to fish or cook, his previous passions, so he now uses his efforts to write. Paralyzed, he uses an infrared sensor to monitor his eye blinks. As the computer program scans the alphabet, he blinks to build words one letter at a time.

Eugenia Chao grew up in California and Taipei City, Taiwan. She currently is pursuing an MFA in fiction at Penn State. "Silence Manager" comes from a larger manuscript, *A Bowl of the Real Thing*. Eugenia's writing is forthcoming or has appeared in *The Cream City Review, Potomac Review,* and *The New Review of Literature*. She also writes for and helps edit a Middle Eastern dance journal, *The Gilded Serpent*.

Elizabeth Biller Chapman's work has appeared in *Prairie Schooner, Poet Lore, BlueLine, Yankee, POETRY,* and *Best American Poetry, 2002*. Her chapbook, *Creekwalker*, won the (M)other Tongue Press international competition. Her poetry collection, *First Orchard*, was published by Bellowing Ark Press. *Candlefish*, her second collection, was chosen as one of four books to inaugurate the new poetry series of the University of Arkansas Press. Chapman lives in Palo Alto, California.

Zdravka Evtimova has published six collections of short stories and three novels. She has received numerous international awards for her writing. Her work has been published in the UK, USA, Canada, Germany, France, India, Argentina, Russia, Poland, Hungary, Czech Republic, Macedonia, and Serbia. Evtimova lives with her husband, two sons, and daughter in Pernik, Bulgaria.

Alice Rose George's poems have been published in *The Paris Review, Bomb Magazine, The New Republic, Fence,* and *The Atlantic*. Her poetry collection, *Ceiling of the World*, was published in 1997 by Spuyten Duyvil. She lives and works in New York City as a photography editor and curator.

Amy Hempel is the author of four collections of short stories, most recently *The Dog of the Marriage*. Her stories have appeared in *Harper's, Vanity Fair, GQ,* and *The Quarterly*. She teaches in the graduate writing program at Bennington College, and lives in New York City.

Judy Katz received her MFA in poetry from Sarah Lawrence College, where she studied with Marie Howe, Billy Collins, and Vijay Seshadri. Her poems have appeared in *The New York Times Book Review, Big City Lit, Lumina, Salamander,* and *The Women's Review of Books*. Judy works as a producer in public television and documentary film. She lives in New York City with her husband and two children.

Jennifer Santos Madriaga resides in Henderson, North Carolina. Her fiction and poetry have appeared in *Bamboo Ridge* and *Crab Creek Review*.

Bryan Maxwell lives in California, where he is a medical student at Stanford University. His work has appeared or is forthcoming in *The Louisville Review, The Eleventh Muse, The Village Rambler, Curbside Review, Word Choice,* and an anthology of medical creative writing.

Rebecca McClanahan has published four volumes of poetry, mostly recently *Naked As Eve;* three books about writing, including *Word Painting: A Guide to Writing More Descriptively;* and a book of personal essays entitled *The Riddle Song and Other Rememberings.* Her work has appeared in *The Best American Essays, The Best American Poetry, Georgia Review, Gettysburg Review,* and *Kenyon Review.* McClanahan, who received a Pushcart Prize in Fiction, the Wood prize from *Poetry,* and (twice) the Carter prize, lives with her husband in New York City.

Margot Zucker Mindich's work has appeared in *Creative Writers Journal, Lynx Eye, Nimrod* and the *Paterson Review.* She was a finalist for the 2002 Nimrod/ Hardman Award, and was recently nominated for a Pushcart Prize. She has recently completed a collection of poems inspired by five decades of stories from her extended family, who emigrated from Paris during WWII. The collection ends with poems about their children and hers.

Patricia O'Hara's personal essays have appeared in *The Sycamore Review, Yale Journal for the Humanities in Medicine, Newsweek,* and *Archives of Psychiatric Nursing.* She is completing a memoir, presently titled *Fall Back,* from which "Stories from the Other Side of Silence" is excerpted. She chairs the English Department at Franklin & Marshall College, where she teaches Victorian literature and creative nonfiction.

Joseph Carlton Porter was born in 1948. His father was a civil engineer, his mother a registered nurse. Following college, he enlisted in the army and served in Vietnam. Intent on becoming a writer, he studied fiction writing at Syracuse University and later graduated from the Iowa Writers' Workshop. He had worked as a newspaper reporter, and currently is an adjunct professor at Onondaga Community College in Syracuse.

Joy Rhoades was raised in a small country town in rural Australia. She qualified as a lawyer in Sydney and has lived and worked in London, Hong Kong, Singapore, and Japan. She has made her home in New York since 2000. Isolation and dislocation are important themes in her work.

Susan Rich is author of *The Cartographer's Tongue / Poems of the World,* which won the PEN West Poetry Award and the Peace Corps Writers Award. She received a Fulbright Fellowship to South Africa, worked for Amnesty International, and has been an electoral supervisor in Bosnia. Her poems appear in *North American Review, Poetry International,* and *Witness.* Rich's collection, *Cures Include Travel,* is forthcoming from White Pine Press. She lives in Seattle.

Katherine Riegel's work has appeared most recently in *88: A Journal of Contemporary American Poetry, Clackamas Literary Review,* and the *Cimarron Review.* She lives in Oswego, New York.

Harriet Rzetelny is a psychotherapist in private practice and Associate Professor at the Shirley Ehrenkranz School of Social Work at New York University. Her short fiction has been published in *Alfred Hitchcock's Mystery Magazine,* and she has had film scripts produced for the American Cancer Society and the Food and Drug Administration.

Whitney Scharer lives in Somerville, Massachusetts, where she works as the program administrator for Grub Street Writers, a non-profit literary arts center. Currently, she is at work on a collection of linked short stories. Whitney received an MFA from the University of Washington, where she was the recipient of the Loren D. Milliman fellowship. Her work has appeared in the *Cimarron Review* and *Mare Nostrum.*

Steven Schwartz is the author of two collections of stories, *To Leningrad in Winter* and *Lives of the Fathers,* and two novels, *Therapy* and *A Good Doctor's Son.* His fiction has received the Nelson Algren Award, the Colorado Book Award, the Sherwood Anderson Prize, and two O. Henry Awards. He directs the MFA Program in Creative Writing at Colorado State University.

Floyd Skloot's most recent book is the memoir *In the Shadow of Memory,* which won the 2004 PEN Center USA Literary Award. Louisiana State University Press will publish his fourth collection of poetry, *The End of Dreams,* and Tupelo Press will publish his fifth, *Approximately Paradise.* He lives in Amity, Oregon.

Alan Steinberg lives and works in upstate New York. He recently has published fiction and poetry in *Peregrine, The Litchfield Review,* and *Blueline.* St. Martin's Press has published his novel, *Cry of the Leopard.*

Virginia Chase Sutton's new book of poetry, *Embellishments,* was published in 2003. Sutton has been the recipient of many national awards. Her work has appeared in *The Paris Review, Antioch Review, Ploughshares, Western Humanities Review, Bellevue Literary Review,* and *Witness.* She currently is at work on a collection of poetry and a book of creative nonfiction.

Lois Taylor was born in Vancouver, Canada. She has won a fiction award from *Story Magazine,* and a poetry award from the Associated Writing Program. Her work has appeared in *The Nation, The Yale Review, StoryQuarterly, Glimmer Train,* and *Mid-American Review.*

John Thompson lives in Media, Pennsylvania, with his wife Jayne and six cats. His work has appeared in *Raven Chronicles, Bayou, Northeast Corridor, Piedmont Literary Review, Widener Review* and *Working Hard for the Money: America's Working Poor,* an anthology published by Bottom Dog Press. Philadelphia's InterAct Theatre Company's "Writing Aloud" has read his work. After decades at various jobs, he now tutors writing, and rehabs houses in "his own time."

Angela Wheelock has worked as a journalist, teacher, and archivist, and now is an editor and writer. Her essays have appeared in *Notre Dame Magazine, Milkweed Press's Liveable Cities Website,* and a forthcoming piece in *Geist.* Wheelock lived for more than a decade in the Yukon, but has recently moved to Vancouver, British Columbia where she lives with her husband, son, and cat. She is currently working on a mystery set in the Yukon and on a memoir.

Gayle Whittier has published fiction in *Editors' Choice,* two Pushcart Prize anthologies, and elsewhere. Her work is forthcoming in *Primavera.* She teaches Literature and Medicine at Binghamton University, where she formerly directed the Creative Writing Program.

Richard Wollman's first full-length poetry collection will be published in 2005 by The Sheep Meadow Press. He is the author of a chapbook, *A Cemetery Affair.* New poems appear or are forthcoming in *New England Review, Prairie Schooner, American Literary Review, Crazyhorse,* and at *Poetry Daily.* He teaches literature and creative writing in Boston at Simmons College.

Acknowledgements

The *Bellevue Literary Review* would like to express its deep gratitude to all who have helped support the journal in its efforts to bridge the worlds of literature and medicine.

Founder: The Vilcek Foundation

Publishers: Anonymous, Dr. Alec Goldenberg, Lenox Hill Hospital

Benefactors: H. Dale & Elizabeth Hemmerdinger, Rita J. & Stanley H. Kaplan Family Foundation, Drs. Anthony & Elayne Mustalish, Pfizer Inc.

Muses: Anonymous, Dr. Katherine Mathews, Lynne Mijangos, Eleanor & Gerard Piel, Mieko Willoughby

Friends: Dr. Edward L. Amorosi, Dr. Felice Aull, Dr. Frances Bailen-Rose, Dr. Michael S. Bruno, Dr. Ralph Crawshaw, Lola Finkelstein, Maggie Jacobs, Dr. Martin L. Kahn, Dr. Sandra Kammerman, Dr. Mark S. Lipton, Dr. Robert Maslansky, Dr. William Schaffner, Dr. Jeffrey M. Shapiro

Supporters: Dr. Michael Attubato, Dr. Tracy Breen, Dr. Max E. Cytryn, Dr. & Mrs. Jonathan Florman, Dr. Arthur Charles Fox, Dr. Joan Cusack Handler, Dr. Charles S. Hirsch, Bernice L. Lewis, Dr. Arthur E. Lindner, Dr. Sander H. Mendelson, Dr. Franco Muggia, Dr. Diana Nilsen, Dr. Emilia Sedlis, Dr. Rhonda L. Soricelli, Gilbert Tauber

----

We welcome your support as we continue to explore the connections between literature and medicine. All patrons will be recognized in the journal.

$75 (Supporter) $150 (Friend) $250 (Muse) - *includes one-year subscription for you and a friend*
$500 (Benefactor) $1000 (Publisher) - *includes three-year subscription for you and a friend*
$10,000 (Founder) - *includes life-time subscription*

The *Bellevue Literary Review* is part of NYU School of Medicine, a 501(c)(3) charitable organization. All contributions are tax-deductible. Please make checks payable to *Bellevue Literary Review*.

Bellevue Literary Review, Department of Medicine, NYU School of Medicine
550 First Avenue, OBV-A612, New York, NY 10016
www.BLReview.org